Taste of Home's

Diabetic Cookbook 2006

Taste of Home Books

Editor: Heidi Reuter Lloyd
Food Editor: Janaan Cunningham
Associate Food Editor: Diane Werner, R.D.
Recipe Editor: Janet Briggs

Nutritional Analysis: Linda R. Yoakam, M.S., R.D., L.D.

Front cover photography by Reiman Publications.
Photographer: Rob Hagen

Pictured on the front cover: Turkey Vegetable Crescent Pie *(page 73).*

Pictured on the back cover *(clockwise from top right):* Italian Crouton Salad *(page 106),* Lemon Meringue Pie *(page 169)* and Broccoli-Cheese Quesadilla *(page 14).*

ISBN: 1-4127-2394-9

ISSN: 1554-0103

Manufactured in China.

8 7 6 5 4 3 2 1

Nutritional Analysis: The nutritional information that appears with each recipe was submitted in part by the participating companies and associations. Every effort has been made to check the accuracy of these numbers. However, because numerous variables account for a wide range of values for certain foods, nutritive analyses in this book should be considered approximate.

Microwave Cooking: Microwave ovens vary in wattage. Use the cooking times as guidelines and check for doneness before adding more time.

Preparation/Cooking Times: Preparation times are based on the approximate amount of time required to assemble the recipe before cooking, baking, chilling or serving. These times include preparation steps such as measuring, chopping and mixing. The fact that some preparations and cooking can be done simultaneously is taken into account. Preparation of optional ingredients and serving suggestions is not included.

Note: This book is for informational purposes and is not intended to provide medical advice. Neither Publications International, Ltd., nor the authors, editors or publisher take responsibility for any possible consequences from any treatment, procedure, exercise, dietary modification, action, or applications of medication or preparation by any person reading or following the information in this cookbook. The publication of this book does not constitute the practice of medicine, and this cookbook does not attempt to replace your physician or your pharmacist. **Before undertaking any course of treatment, the authors, editors and publisher advise the reader to check with a physician or other health care provider.**

Taste of Home's Diabetic Cookbook 2006

Personalizing Your Healthy Lifestyle

Cavatelli and Vegetable Stir-Fry (page 98)

EATING WELL JUST GOT EASIER

Here's good news!

Eating well just got easier, thanks to *Taste of Home's Diabetic Cookbook 2006*. You have in your hands the third edition of this helpful series.

You may think that people with diabetes need special foods prepared in special ways. Actually, the best recipes for someone with diabetes are no different than great recipes for everyone.

To prove that point, we've put together this cookbook. It offers an abundance of easy, delicious recipes your entire family will enjoy.

As you look through the 216 recipes, you'll be surprised to see the wide variety of foods prepared with an assortment of delectable ingredients and seasonings.

These appealing recipes have been carefully created using low-fat, healthy ingredients that are readily available in most grocery stores. We cover the full range—from breakfast to dinner, plus desserts and snacks.

We've made this book easy to use with quick-glance symbols denoting low-fat, low-sodium, low-carbohydrate, high-fiber and meatless recipes. That way you don't necessarily have to look through the nutritional information to find a recipe that meets your needs. (See page 7 for a guide to the symbols used in this book and other helpful information.)

Preparation and cooking times are streamlined too, complementing today's busy lifestyles. In fact, the quick-to-make recipes are highlighted so you can easily find them.

With this unique cookbook, you can bring family favorites to the table so your whole family can gain the rewards of eating well and enjoying every meal.

Diane Werner, R.D.

LOWER FAT, NOT FLAVOR

Here are a few tips for increasing flavor without adding fat and calories:

- Substitute ground turkey in recipes calling for ground beef to lower the fat content. Be sure to choose turkey labeled as extra-lean or 95% fat-free or higher.

- Make soups and stews the day before you plan to serve them. After your preparation is complete, refrigerate them so fat will solidify on top. Remove this fat before reheating.

- Be sure to remove the skin from poultry. Chicken parts can be skinned, then breaded and baked. This is a good low-fat substitute for fried chicken.

- To lower fat, calories and cholesterol, replace full-fat cheeses in recipes with those that are less than 6 grams of fat per ounce. Or if you prefer full-fat cheese, cut the amount you use in half by using shredded or stronger flavored cheeses (such as sharp Cheddar or Parmesan).

- To add flavor and juiciness, try marinating meat and poultry in wine-flavored vinegar, juice or fat-free dressings instead of oil-based marinades.

- Rather than adding butter or margarine, flavor vegetables with fat-free broth, garlic, lemon juice, minced onion or flavored vinegars.

- Choose whole grain bread, pasta and crackers to increase the fiber in your diet. Substitute whole wheat flour for up to half of the all-purpose flour called for in a recipe to add fiber to baked goods. Fiber adds bulk, which tends to help you feel full without a lot of added calories.

- To lower cholesterol and fat in recipes, substitute 2 egg whites for 1 whole egg. This will save 213 milligrams of cholesterol for every large egg you replace.

- For perfect grilled vegetables, grill them 4 to 5 inches from medium heat. Prevent the vegetables from drying out by brushing them with fat-free salad dressings or a small amount of olive oil. Spray the grill rack with nonstick cooking spray before heating the grill to keep the vegetables from sticking and to make cleanup easier.

EAT OUT, EAT RIGHT

Here are some tips for dining at restaurants:

- Request that salad dressings, sauces and gravies be served on the side.

- Beware of huge portions. Eat the same amount you usually eat at home and bring the rest home to enjoy tomorrow.

- Consider ordering from the children's or seniors' menu. Portion sizes are smaller and more reasonable. Sometimes you may need to inform the server that you have diabetes before being able to choose from these menus.

- If you are at a chain restaurant, a nutrient analysis of the menu items may be available. Ask for the information to aid in making healthy choices.

- For trips or long commutes, pack some fresh fruit, cut-up vegetables, low-fat string cheese or a handful of unsalted nuts to help you avoid impulsive, less healthful snacks.

- Choose low-fat appetizers such as broth-based soup, shrimp cocktail, steamed clams or fresh fruit.

- Learn the key words for low-fat preparation: steamed, in its own juice, broiled, grilled, roasted and poached.

MEAL-PLANNING APPROACHES– EXCHANGES/CARBOHYDRATE COUNTING

People with diabetes can choose from several meal-planning approaches. Regardless of the plan used, one principle remains a common factor—all meal plans are designed to encourage you to eat similar amounts of carbohydrate at similar times each day.

EXCHANGE LISTS AND THE EXCHANGE SYSTEM

The exchange system categorizes foods into three main groups: carbohydrates, proteins and fats. An exchange system meal plan doesn't dictate what foods you eat. Instead, you choose from "exchange lists" of foods with similar nutritional make-up. For example, foods from the carbohydrate/starch group—such as a slice of bread, a small baked potato or 3/4 cup of unsweetened dry cereal—all have about the same amount of carbohydrate, protein and fat. Therefore, they are all exchangeable with each other.

An advantage of the exchange system is that it's still the common language used for communicating about food and diabetes. Cookbooks, magazine food articles and even some food labels use it.

CARBOHYDRATE COUNTING

Carbohydrate counting is keeping track of the number of carbohydrate grams you eat each day, not the individual foods. An individualized meal plan is designed so you eat a specific number of carbohydrate grams at each meal and snack. You then choose foods that total the specified number of carbohydrates.

Carbohydrate counting is based on the fact that within one to two hours of eating, 90% to 100% of digestible starches and sugars turn up in your blood as glucose. So the amount of carbohydrate you eat may also determine the amount of medication you need to cover the rise in blood glucose from meals and snacks.

How do you know how many grams of carbohydrate are in foods? The Nutrition Facts panel on packaged foods lists the grams of carbohydrate in a serving.

Every recipe in this book lists grams of carbohydrate per serving, as well as the exchange information. An advantage of carbohydrate counting is you only keep track of carbs, instead of all components of your diet.

Q & A

1. Why is fish such a healthy choice?
Besides being an excellent source of protein, most seafood is low in fat, especially saturated fat. Fish also contain omega-3 fatty acids, substances that may help reduce heart disease, joint pain and other rheumatoid problems, as well as help our brains, central nervous system and membranes throughout the body stay healthy. The best sources are fatty fish such as albacore tuna, salmon, mackerel, sardines and lake trout. The American Heart Association recommends eating 2 fish meals (3 to 4 ounces each) per week to receive the protective benefits.

2. My doctor told me to follow the DASH diet to help my blood pressure. What is DASH?
Dietary Approaches to Stop Hypertension (DASH) is an eating plan that has been shown to lower blood pressure. Goals include: incorporating 2 to 3 fat-free or low-fat dairy products (for calcium) and 8 to 10 fruits and vegetables (for vitamins and minerals) daily. Sodium and alcohol intake should be limited, and low-fat cooking techniques emphasized.

3. What are trans fats and where do I find them?
Trans fatty acids, or "trans fats," are formed when manufacturers turn liquid oils into solid fats. This process, called hydrogenation, increases the shelf life and flavor stability of foods. Trans fats are found in many foods such as margarine, shortening, crackers, cookies, granola bars, chips and snack foods. Trans fats act like saturated fats, potentially raising LDL (bad) cholesterol and lowering HDL (good) cholesterol, thereby increasing heart disease risk. The good news is that effective January 1, 2006, trans fats will be listed on nutrition labels.

HOW NUTRITIONAL ANALYSES WERE CALCULATED

• When a choice of ingredients is given in a recipe (such as 1/3 cup of sour cream or plain yogurt), the first ingredient listed was the one used for calculating the Nutrients per Serving.

• Recipe or plate garnishes were not included in the calculations.

• Optional ingredients were not included in the calculations.

• When a range was given (such as 2 to 3 teaspoons), the first amount listed was used.

• Only the amount of marinade absorbed during preparation was used in the calculations.

ABOUT THE ICONS

You will find special icons included with many recipes in the book. With these, you can determine at a glance which recipes fit your needs. Here is a simple explanation of the icons:

 low fat 3 grams or less per serving

 low sodium 140 milligrams or less per serving

 low carb 10 grams or less per serving

Quick Recipe: 30 minutes or less total preparation and cook time

 high fiber 5 grams or more per serving

 meatless includes eggs and dairy products

 cooking for 1 or 2 recipe serves 1 or 2 people

ADDITIONAL RESOURCES

If you have not met with a diabetes educator or attended a diabetes education class, ask your doctor or healthcare provider about educational opportunities. A registered dietitian can help you make good food choices and can also help you understand your personal meal plan.

Here are two websites to visit for current news and information about diabetes:

www.diabeteshealth.com

www.diabetesmonitor.com

GROCERY SHOPPING TIPS

Here are a few ideas to help you make good choices in the grocery store:

• Before you head to the grocery store, take some time for planning. First, make a list of meal ideas for the week, keeping in mind which days you will have time to cook from scratch and which days you will be pressed for time to put dinner on the table.

• Use the nutrition labels to compare the nutrients and ingredients in similar products. Choosing items with 3 grams of fat or less per serving will help keep your diet heart-healthy.

• Try adding more beans, peas and lentils to your diet. There are many varieties, both dry and canned, available in the supermarket. Beans such as pinto, black and kidney are low in fat and rich in fiber, folate and protein.

• If you find it too time-consuming to clean and chop vegetables, consider purchasing some items already cleaned and cut up (from the produce aisle or salad bar). Combined with precut meat or poultry strips, a stir-fry becomes a fast, easy-to-prepare dinner.

• The U.S. Dietary Guidelines encourage us to eat 3 servings of whole grains daily. A bread that is brown or labeled as 7-grain or multi-grain isn't necessarily made from whole wheat. Look for bread labels that list 100% whole wheat as the first ingredient. Other whole grains to try are brown rice, bulgur, oats, corn (hominy), whole rye and barley.

Appetizers

❧ ❧ ❧

Fast Guacamole and 'Chips'

low sodium — low carb — meatless

Quick Recipe   *(Pictured at left)*

    2 ripe avocados
    1/2 cup prepared chunky salsa
    1/4 teaspoon hot pepper sauce (optional)
    1/2 seedless cucumber, sliced into 1/8-inch-thick rounds

1. Cut avocados in half; remove and discard pits. Scoop flesh into medium bowl. Mash with fork.

2. Add salsa and hot pepper sauce, if desired; mix well.

3. Transfer guacamole to serving bowl; serve with cucumber 'chips.'   *Makes 8 servings (about 1-3/4 cups)*

Nutrients per Serving: about 3-1/2 tablespoons guacamole with cucumber 'chips'

Calories 85	**Fiber** 2g
Fat 7g (sat 1g)	**Cholesterol** 0mg
Protein 2g	**Sodium** 120mg
Carbohydrate 5g	

Exchanges: 1 vegetable, 1-1/2 fat

Clockwise from top left: *Asian Vegetable Rolls with Soy-Lime Dipping Sauce (page 12), Broccoli-Cheese Quesadilla (page 14), Fast Guacamole and 'Chips' and Crab Cakes Canton (page 16)*

Cold Asparagus with Lemon-Mustard Dressing

(Pictured at right)

- 12 fresh asparagus spears
- 2 tablespoons fat-free mayonnaise
- 1 tablespoon prepared sweet brown mustard
- 1 tablespoon fresh lemon juice
- 1 teaspoon grated lemon peel, divided

1. Steam asparagus until crisp-tender and bright green; immediately drain and rinse under cold water. Cover and refrigerate until chilled.

2. Combine mayonnaise, mustard and lemon juice in small bowl; blend well. Stir in 1/2 teaspoon lemon peel; set aside.

3. Divide asparagus between 2 plates. Spoon 2 tablespoons dressing over top of each serving; sprinkle each with 1/4 teaspoon lemon peel.
Makes 2 servings

Nutrients per Serving: 6 asparagus spears with 2 tablespoons dressing

Calories 39	**Fiber** 2g
Fat 1g (sat <1g)	**Cholesterol** 0mg
Protein 3g	**Sodium** 294mg
Carbohydrate 7g	

Exchanges: 1-1/2 vegetable

Cranberry Walnut Pear Wedges

- 1/4 cup orange juice
- 2 tablespoons honey
- 2 tablespoons balsamic vinegar
- 3 medium ripe pears, quartered and cored
- 1/2 cup prepared cranberry fruit relish
- 1/4 cup finely chopped walnuts
- 1/4 cup crumbled blue cheese

1. Combine orange juice, honey and vinegar in large resealable plastic bag. Add pears. Seal bag; turn several times to coat pears evenly. Refrigerate at least 1 hour, turning bag occasionally.

2. Drain pears; discard marinade. Place pears on serving platter. Spoon cranberry relish evenly into cavities of pears; sprinkle with walnuts and cheese.
Makes 12 servings

Nutrients per Serving: 1 pear wedge

Calories 77	**Fiber** 1g
Fat 3g (sat 1g)	**Cholesterol** 2mg
Protein 1g	**Sodium** 43mg
Carbohydrate 13g	

Exchanges: 1 fruit, 1/2 fat

Cold Asparagus with Lemon-Mustard Dressing

Asian Vegetable Rolls with Soy-Lime Dipping Sauce

Quick Recipe   *(Pictured on page 8)*

- 1/4 cup reduced-sodium soy sauce
- 2 tablespoons lime juice
- 1 teaspoon honey
- 1 clove garlic, crushed
- 1/2 teaspoon finely chopped fresh gingerroot
- 1/4 teaspoon dark sesame oil
- 1/8 to 1/4 teaspoon dried red pepper flakes
- 1/2 cup grated cucumber
- 1/3 cup grated carrot
- 1/4 cup thinly sliced 1-inch yellow bell pepper strips
- 2 tablespoons thinly sliced green onion
- 18 small leaf or Bibb lettuce leaves from inner part of head
- Sesame seeds (optional)

1. Combine soy sauce, lime juice, honey, garlic, gingerroot, oil and red pepper flakes in small bowl.

2. Combine cucumber, carrot, bell pepper and green onion in medium bowl.

3. Add 1 tablespoon soy sauce mixture to vegetable mixture; stir to combine.

4. Place about 1 tablespoon vegetable mixture on each lettuce leaf. Roll up leaves and top with sesame seeds at time of serving, if desired. Serve with remaining sauce.   *Makes 6 servings*

Nutrients per Serving: 3 rolls with 1 tablespoon dipping sauce

Calories 25	**Fiber** 1g
Fat <1g (sat <1g)	**Cholesterol** 0mg
Protein 1g	**Sodium** 343mg
Carbohydrate 5g	

Exchanges: Free

Marinated Artichokes & Shrimp in Citrus Vinaigrette

Vinaigrette
- 1 large seedless orange, peeled and sectioned
- 3 tablespoons fat-free mayonnaise
- 3 tablespoons red wine vinegar
- 1 teaspoon fresh thyme *or* 1/4 teaspoon dried thyme leaves
- 2 teaspoons olive oil

Salad
- 1 package (9 ounces) frozen artichoke hearts, thawed
- 12 large uncooked shrimp (about 3/4 pound)
- 1 cup orange juice

1. To prepare vinaigrette, combine all vinaigrette ingredients except oil in blender or food processor; cover and process until smooth. Pour mixture into medium nonmetal bowl and whisk in oil until blended.

2. Fold artichoke hearts into vinaigrette. Cover and refrigerate several hours or overnight.

3. Peel shrimp, leaving tails attached. Devein and butterfly shrimp. Bring orange juice to a boil in medium saucepan. Add shrimp and cook about 2 minutes or just until shrimp turn pink and opaque.

4. To serve, place about 3 artichoke hearts on each of 6 plates. Top each serving with 2 shrimp. Drizzle vinaigrette over top.

Makes 6 servings

Nutrients per Serving: 1 serving

Calories 135	**Fiber** 4g
Fat 2g (sat <1g)	**Cholesterol** 87mg
Protein 12g	**Sodium** 236mg
Carbohydrate 19g	

Exchanges: 1 fruit, 1 vegetable, 1-1/2 lean meat

Chutney Cheese Spread

(Pictured below)

- 2 packages (8 ounces each) fat-free cream cheese
- 1 cup shredded reduced-fat Cheddar cheese
- 1/2 cup mango chutney
- 1/4 cup thinly sliced green onions
- 3 tablespoons dark raisins, chopped
- 2 cloves garlic, minced
- 1 to 1-1/2 teaspoons curry powder
- 3/4 teaspoon ground coriander
- 1/2 to 3/4 teaspoon ground ginger
- 1 tablespoon chopped dry-roasted peanuts

1. Place cream cheese and Cheddar cheese in food processor or blender; cover and process until smooth. Stir in chutney, green onions, raisins, garlic, curry powder, coriander and ginger. Cover; refrigerate 2 to 3 hours.

2. Top spread with peanuts. Serve with additional green onions and melba toast, if desired. *Makes 20 servings*

Hint: This spread can also be garnished with one tablespoon toasted coconut to provide a slightly sweeter flavor.

Nutrients per Serving: 2 tablespoons spread

Calories 58	**Fiber** <1g
Fat 1g (sat <1g)	**Cholesterol** 7mg
Protein 5g	**Sodium** 218mg
Carbohydrate 7g	

Exchanges: 1/2 starch, 1/2 lean meat

Chutney Cheese Spread

Vegetable & Couscous Filled Tomatoes

Quick Recipe   *(Pictured at right)*

- **1/2 cup fat-free reduced-sodium chicken broth**
- **2 teaspoons olive oil**
- **1/3 cup uncooked couscous**
- **18 large plum tomatoes**
- **1 cup diced zucchini**
- **1/3 cup sliced green onions**
- **2 cloves garlic, minced**
- **2 tablespoons finely chopped fresh Italian parsley**
- **1-1/2 teaspoons Dijon mustard**
- **1/2 teaspoon dried Italian seasoning**

1. Place chicken broth and oil in small saucepan; bring to a boil over high heat. Stir in couscous; cover. Remove saucepan from heat; let stand 5 minutes.

2. Cut thin slice from top of each tomato. Remove pulp, leaving 1/8-inch-thick shell; reserve pulp. Place tomatoes, cut side down, on paper towels to drain. Meanwhile, drain excess liquid from reserved pulp. Chop pulp to measure 2/3 cup.

3. Spray large nonstick skillet with nonstick cooking spray; heat over medium heat until hot. Add zucchini, onions and garlic. Cook and stir 5 minutes or until vegetables are tender.

4. Combine couscous, reserved tomato pulp, vegetables, parsley, mustard and Italian seasoning in large bowl. Fill tomato shells evenly with couscous mixture.

Makes 18 servings

Nutrients per Serving: 1 filled tomato

Calories 33	**Fiber** 1g
Fat 1g (sat <1g)	**Cholesterol** 0mg
Protein 1g	**Sodium** 29mg
Carbohydrate 6g	

Exchanges: 1 vegetable

Broccoli-Cheese Quesadillas

Quick Recipe   *(Pictured on page 8)*

- **1 cup shredded fat-free Cheddar cheese**
- **1/2 cup finely chopped fresh broccoli**
- **2 tablespoons prepared picante sauce or salsa**
- **4 (6- to 7-inch) corn or flour tortillas**
- **1 teaspoon butter, divided**

1. Combine cheese, broccoli and picante sauce in small bowl; mix well.

2. Spoon 1/4 of cheese mixture onto 1 side of each tortilla; fold tortilla over filling.

3. Melt 1/2 teaspoon butter in 10-inch nonstick skillet over medium heat. Add 2 quesadillas; cook about 2 minutes on each side or until tortillas are golden brown and cheese is melted. Repeat with remaining 1/2 teaspoon butter and 2 quesadillas.

Makes 4 servings

Nutrients per Serving: 1 quesadilla

Calories 109	**Fiber** 1g
Fat 2g (sat <1g)	**Cholesterol** 5mg
Protein 11g	**Sodium** 313mg
Carbohydrate 14g	

Exchanges: 1 starch, 1 lean meat

Vegetable & Couscous Filled Tomatoes

Crab Cakes Canton

Quick Recipe   *(Pictured on page 8)*

> 7 ounces thawed frozen cooked crabmeat or imitation crabmeat, drained and flaked
> 1-1/2 cups fresh whole wheat bread crumbs (about 3 slices bread)
> 1/4 cup thinly sliced green onions
> 1 teaspoon minced fresh gingerroot
> 1 clove garlic, minced
> 2 egg whites, lightly beaten
> 1 tablespoon teriyaki sauce
> 2 teaspoons canola oil, divided
> Prepared sweet-and-sour sauce (optional)

1. Combine crabmeat, bread crumbs, onions, gingerroot and garlic in medium bowl; mix well. Add egg whites and teriyaki sauce; mix well. Shape into 12 patties about 1/2 inch thick and 2 inches in diameter.*

2. Heat 1 teaspoon oil in large nonstick skillet over medium heat until hot. Add half of crab cakes to skillet. Cook 2 minutes per side or until golden brown. Remove to warm serving plate; keep warm. Repeat with remaining 1 teaspoon oil and crab cakes. Serve with sweet-and-sour sauce, if desired.   *Makes 6 servings*

*Crab cakes may be made ahead to this point; cover and refrigerate up to 24 hours before cooking.

Nutrients per Serving: 2 crab cakes

Calories 84	**Fiber** <1g
Fat 2g (sat <1g)	**Cholesterol** 18mg
Protein 9g	**Sodium** 480mg
Carbohydrate 6g	

Exchanges: 1/2 starch, 1 lean meat

Roasted Garlic Spread with Three Cheeses

> 2 medium heads garlic
> 2 packages (8 ounces each) fat-free cream cheese, softened
> 1 package (3-1/2 ounces) goat cheese
> 2 tablespoons crumbled blue cheese
> 1 teaspoon dried thyme leaves
> Assorted sliced fresh vegetables for dipping (optional)

1. Preheat oven to 400°F. Cut tops off garlic heads to expose tops of cloves. Place garlic in small baking pan; bake 45 minutes or until garlic is very tender. Remove from pan; cool completely. Squeeze garlic into small bowl; mash with fork.

2. Beat cream cheese and goat cheese in small bowl until smooth; stir in blue cheese, garlic and thyme. Cover; refrigerate 3 hours or overnight.

3. Spoon dip into serving bowl; serve with sliced cucumbers, radishes, carrots or yellow bell peppers, if desired.   *Makes 21 servings*

Nutrients per Serving: 2 tablespoons spread

Calories 37	**Fiber** <1g
Fat 1g (sat <1g)	**Cholesterol** 9mg
Protein 4g	**Sodium** 157mg
Carbohydrate 2g	

Exchanges: 1/2 lean meat

Roast Beef Roll-Ups

Quick Recipe

- 2 tablespoons fat-free mayonnaise
- 1/2 teaspoon prepared horseradish
- 2 slices deli roast beef (about 1 ounce each)
- 6 tablespoons crumbled blue cheese
- 2 thin slices red onion, quartered

Combine mayonnaise and horseradish in small bowl, spread over 1 side of each roast beef slice. Top each slice with blue cheese and onion. Roll up each slice tightly to make 2 rolls.

Makes 2 servings

Nutrients per Serving: 1 Roll-Up

Calories 124	**Fiber** 1g
Fat 7g (sat 4g)	**Cholesterol** 36mg
Protein 10g	**Sodium** 567mg
Carbohydrate 4g	

Exchanges: 1/2 vegetable, 1-1/2 lean meat, 1 fat

Tortellini Teasers

Quick Recipe   *(Pictured at right)*

- Zesty Tomato Sauce (recipe follows)
- 1/2 (9-ounce) package refrigerated cheese tortellini
- 1 large red or green bell pepper, cut into 1-inch pieces
- 2 medium carrots, peeled and sliced 1/2 inch thick
- 1 medium zucchini, sliced 1/2 inch thick
- 12 medium fresh mushrooms
- 12 fresh cherry tomatoes

1. Prepare Zesty Tomato Sauce; keep warm.

2. Cook tortellini according to package directions; drain.

3. Alternate tortellini and vegetable pieces on 6 wooden skewers. Serve with tomato sauce.

Makes 6 servings

Zesty Tomato Sauce

- 1 can (15 ounces) tomato purée
- 2 tablespoons finely chopped onion
- 2 tablespoons chopped fresh parsley
- 1 teaspoon dried oregano leaves
- 1/4 teaspoon dried thyme leaves
- 1/4 teaspoon salt
- 1/8 teaspoon black pepper

Combine tomato purée, onion, parsley, oregano and thyme in small saucepan. Heat thoroughly, stirring occasionally. Stir in salt and pepper.

Nutrients per Serving: 1 kabob with about 1/4 cup tomato sauce

Calories 130	**Fiber** 5g
Fat 2g (sat 1g)	**Cholesterol** 12mg
Protein 7g	**Sodium** 306mg
Carbohydrate 23g	

Exchanges: 1 starch, 2 vegetable, 1/2 fat

Tortellini Teasers

Herbed Potato Chips

3. Combine dill, garlic salt and pepper in small bowl; sprinkle evenly over potato slices. Continue baking 5 to 10 minutes or until potatoes are golden brown. Cool on baking sheets. Serve with sour cream.

Makes 6 servings

Nutrients per Serving: 10 chips with about 3 tablespoons sour cream

Calories 106	**Fiber** 1g
Fat 2g (sat <1g)	**Cholesterol** 8mg
Protein 4g	**Sodium** 84mg
Carbohydrate 16g	

Exchanges: 1 starch, 1/2 fat

$\sim$ $\sim$ $\sim$

Herbed Potato Chips

Quick Recipe   *(Pictured above)*

> **Nonstick olive oil cooking spray**
> **2 medium red potatoes (about 1/2 pound), unpeeled**
> **1 tablespoon olive oil**
> **2 tablespoons minced fresh dill, thyme or rosemary *or* 2 teaspoons dried dill weed, thyme or rosemary, crushed**
> **1/4 teaspoon garlic salt**
> **1/8 teaspoon black pepper**
> **1-1/4 cups fat-free sour cream**

1. Preheat oven to 450°F. Spray large baking sheets with cooking spray; set aside.

2. Cut potatoes crosswise into very thin slices, about 1/16 inch thick. Pat dry with paper towels. Arrange potato slices in single layer on prepared baking sheets; coat potatoes with cooking spray. Bake 10 minutes; turn slices over. Brush with oil.

Pimiento Cheese Toast

Quick Recipe

> **1 (16-ounce) loaf French bread**
> **1 cup shredded reduced-fat sharp Cheddar cheese**
> **2 tablespoons diced pimiento**
> **2 tablespoons reduced-fat mayonnaise**
> **1 teaspoon lemon juice**
> **1/4 teaspoon dried oregano leaves**

1. Slice bread into 8 (1-inch-thick) slices. Toast lightly in toaster or toaster oven.

2. Combine cheese and pimiento in medium bowl. Combine mayonnaise, lemon juice and oregano in small bowl; stir into cheese mixture. Spread 1 tablespoon mixture onto each slice of toast.

3. Preheat broiler. Place prepared toasts on broiler rack. Broil 4 inches from heat 2 minutes. Serve immediately.

Makes 8 servings

Nutrients per Serving: 1 Cheese Toast

Calories 203	**Fiber** 0g
Fat 5g (sat 1g)	**Cholesterol** 9mg
Protein 8g	**Sodium** 541mg
Carbohydrate 31g	

Exchanges: 2 starch, 1/2 lean meat, 1/2 fat

Almond Chicken Cups

Quick Recipe   *(Pictured below)*

- **1 tablespoon canola oil**
- **1/2 cup chopped red bell pepper**
- **1/2 cup chopped onion**
- **2 cups chopped cooked boneless skinless chicken**
- **2/3 cup prepared sweet-and-sour sauce**
- **1/2 cup chopped almonds**
- **2 tablespoons reduced-sodium soy sauce**
- **6 (7-inch) flour tortillas**

1. Preheat oven to 400°F. Heat oil in small skillet over medium heat until hot. Add bell pepper and onion. Cook and stir 3 minutes or until crisp-tender.

2. Combine chicken, vegetable mixture, sweet-and-sour sauce, almonds and soy sauce in medium bowl; mix until well blended.

3. Cut each tortilla in half. Place each half in 2-3/4-inch muffin cup. Fill each with about 1/4 cup chicken mixture.

4. Bake 8 to 10 minutes or until tortilla edges are crisp and filling is hot. Remove muffin pan to cooling rack. Let stand 5 minutes before serving.   *Makes 12 servings*

Nutrients per Serving: 1 Almond Chicken Cup

Calories 190	**Fiber** 2g
Fat 7g (sat 1g)	**Cholesterol** 21mg
Protein 10g	**Sodium** 282mg
Carbohydrate 22g	

Exchanges: 1-1/2 starch, 1 lean meat, 1 fat

Almond Chicken Cups

BLT Cukes

Quick Recipe   *(Pictured at right)*

> **1/2 cup finely chopped lettuce and fresh baby spinach**
> **1/4 cup diced fresh tomato**
> **3 slices crisp-cooked bacon, chopped**
> **1-1/2 tablespoons fat-free mayonnaise**
> **1/4 teaspoon black pepper**
> **Pinch salt (optional)**
> **1 large cucumber**
> **Green onion or minced fresh parsley (optional)**

1. Combine greens, tomato and bacon with mayonnaise. Season with pepper and salt, if desired; set aside.

2. Peel cucumber. Trim ends, and slice in half lengthwise. Scoop out seeds and discard. Place cucumber in glass dish. Spoon BLT mixture into hollowed-out cucumber halves. Sprinkle with green onion or minced parsley, if desired. Slice into 8 pieces.   *Makes 8 servings*

Note: Make these snacks when cucumbers are plentiful and large enough to easily hollow out with a spoon. You can make these up to 12 hours ahead of time and chill until ready to serve.

Nutrients per Serving: 1 piece

Calories 26	**Fiber** <1g
Fat 2g (sat <1g)	**Cholesterol** 3mg
Protein 2g	**Sodium** 72mg
Carbohydrate 2g	

Exchanges: Free

Quick and Easy Stuffed Mushrooms

Quick Recipe

> **1 slice whole wheat bread**
> **16 large fresh mushrooms**
> **1/2 cup sliced celery**
> **1/2 cup sliced onion**
> **1 clove garlic**
> **Nonstick cooking spray**
> **1 teaspoon Worcestershire sauce**
> **1/2 teaspoon marjoram leaves, crushed**
> **1/8 teaspoon ground red pepper**
> **Dash paprika**

1. Tear bread into pieces; place in food processor. Cover and process 30 seconds or until crumbs form. Transfer to small bowl; set aside.

2. Remove stems from mushrooms; reserve caps. Place mushroom stems, celery, onion and garlic in food processor. Cover and process with on/off pulses until vegetables are finely chopped.

3. Preheat oven to 350°F. Spray nonstick skillet with cooking spray. Add vegetable mixture; cook and stir over medium heat 5 minutes or until onion is tender. Remove to bowl. Stir in bread crumbs, Worcestershire sauce, marjoram and ground red pepper.

4. Fill mushroom caps with mixture, pressing down firmly. Place filled caps in shallow baking dish about 1/2 inch apart. Spray lightly with cooking spray. Sprinkle with paprika. Bake 15 minutes or until hot.   *Makes 8 servings*

Note: Mushrooms can be stuffed up to 1 day ahead. Refrigerate filled mushroom caps, covered, until ready to serve. Bake in preheated 300°F oven 20 minutes or until hot.

Nutrients per Serving: 2 stuffed mushroom caps

Calories 20	**Fiber** 1g
Fat <1g (sat <1g)	**Cholesterol** 0mg
Protein 1g	**Sodium** 29mg
Carbohydrate 4g	

Exchanges: 1 vegetable

BLT Cukes

Oriental Salsa

Quick Recipe   *(Pictured at right)*

> **1 cup diced unpeeled cucumber**
> **1/2 cup chopped red bell pepper**
> **1/2 cup thinly sliced green onions**
> **1/3 cup coarsely chopped fresh cilantro**
> **2 tablespoons reduced-sodium soy sauce**
> **1 tablespoon rice vinegar**
> **1 clove garlic, minced**
> **1/2 teaspoon dark sesame oil**
> **1/4 teaspoon dried red pepper flakes**
> **Easy Wonton Chips (recipe follows) *or* assorted fresh vegetables for dipping**

Combine cucumber, bell pepper, onions, cilantro, soy sauce, rice vinegar, garlic, oil and red pepper flakes in medium bowl until well blended. Cover and refrigerate until serving time. Serve with Easy Wonton Chips or assorted fresh vegetables for dipping.   *Makes 4 servings*

Easy Wonton Chips

> **1 tablespoon reduced-sodium soy sauce**
> **2 teaspoons peanut or canola oil**
> **1/2 teaspoon sugar**
> **1/4 teaspoon garlic salt**
> **12 wonton wrappers**

1. Preheat oven to 375°F. Combine soy sauce, oil, sugar and garlic salt in small bowl; mix well.

2. Cut each wonton wrapper diagonally in half. Place on 15×10-inch jelly-roll pan sprayed with nonstick cooking spray. Brush soy sauce mixture lightly over both sides of wrappers. Bake 4 to 6 minutes or until crisp and lightly browned, turning after 3 minutes. Transfer to cooling rack; cool completely.   *Makes 2 dozen chips*

Nutrients per Serving: 1/4 cup salsa with 6 chips

Calories 103	**Fiber** 1g
Fat 3g (sat <1g)	**Cholesterol** 2mg
Protein 3g	**Sodium** 496mg
Carbohydrate 16g	

Exchanges: 1 starch, 1/2 vegetable, 1/2 fat

Caponata Spread

> **1-1/2 tablespoons BERTOLLI® Olive Oil**
> **1 medium eggplant, diced (about 4 cups)**
> **1 medium onion, chopped**
> **1-1/2 cups water, divided**
> **1 envelope LIPTON® RECIPE SECRETS® Savory Herb with Garlic Soup Mix**
> **2 tablespoons chopped fresh parsley (optional)**
> **Salt and ground black pepper to taste**
> **Pita chips or thinly sliced Italian or French bread**

In 10-inch nonstick skillet, heat oil over medium heat and cook eggplant with onion 3 minutes. Add 1/2 cup water. Reduce heat to low and simmer, covered, 3 minutes. Stir in soup mix blended with remaining 1 cup water. Bring to a boil over high heat. Reduce heat to low and simmer, uncovered, stirring occasionally, 20 minutes. Stir in parsley, salt and pepper. Serve with pita chips.

Makes about 4 cups spread

Nutrients per Serving: 2 tablespoons spread (without salt and pepper seasoning and pita chips)

Calories 13	**Fiber** <1g
Fat 1g (sat <1g)	**Cholesterol** 0mg
Protein <1g	**Sodium** 60mg
Carbohydrate 2g	

Exchanges: Free

Left to right: Easy Wonton Chips and Oriental Salsa

Nachos

Nachos

(Pictured above)

8 (6-inch) corn tortillas
1 cup chopped onion
1 tablespoon chili powder
2 teaspoons dried oregano leaves, crushed
1 can (15 ounces) pinto beans or black beans, rinsed and drained
1-1/4 cups shredded reduced-fat Mexican cheese blend
3/4 cup frozen whole kernel corn, thawed and drained
1 jar (2 ounces) chopped pimientos, drained
3 tablespoons ripe olive slices
2 to 3 tablespoons pickled jalapeño pepper slices,* drained

Jalapeño peppers can sting and irritate the skin. Wear rubber gloves when handling peppers and do not touch your eyes. Wash hands after handling peppers.

1. Preheat oven to 375°F. Sprinkle 1 tortilla with water to dampen; shake off excess water. Repeat with remaining tortillas. Cut each tortilla into 6 wedges. Arrange wedges in single layer on baking sheet or in 2 (9-inch) pie plates. Bake 4 minutes. Rotate sheet. Bake another 2 to 4 minutes or until chips are firm; do not let brown. Remove chips to ovenproof plate to cool. Set aside.

2. Spray bottom of medium saucepan with nonstick cooking spray. Cook and stir onion over medium-high heat 8 to 10 minutes or until onion is tender and begins to brown. Add chili powder and oregano; cook and stir 1 minute more. Remove from heat.

3. Add beans and 2 tablespoons water to saucepan; mash with fork or potato masher until blended, yet chunky. Return to heat. Cover; cook beans, stirring occasionally, 6 to 8 minutes or until bubbly. Stir in additional water if beans become dry. Remove from heat. Set beans aside.

4. Sprinkle cheese evenly over chips. Spoon beans over top.

5. Combine corn and pimientos; spoon over beans. Bake about 8 minutes or until cheese melts. Sprinkle olives and jalapeños over top.
Makes 8 servings

Nutrients per Serving: 6 chips with 1/8 of topping

Calories 185	Fiber 5g
Fat 6g (sat 2g)	Cholesterol 13mg
Protein 10g	Sodium 390mg
Carbohydrate 27g	

Exchanges: 1-1/2 starch, 1 vegetable, 1 lean meat

Tip

Make this dish even simpler by replacing the corn tortillas with 56 packaged baked tortilla chips (7 per serving). Omit the first step and begin with step two. The nutritional information will stay the same.

Baked Spinach Balls

2 cups sage and onion or herb-seasoned bread stuffing mix
1 small onion, chopped
2 tablespoons grated Parmesan cheese
1 clove garlic, minced
1/4 teaspoon dried thyme leaves
1/4 teaspoon black pepper
1 package (10 ounces) frozen chopped spinach, thawed and well drained
1/4 cup fat-free reduced-sodium chicken broth
2 egg whites, beaten
Dijon or honey mustard (optional)

1. Combine bread stuffing mix, onion, cheese, garlic, thyme and pepper in medium bowl; mix well.

2. Combine spinach, broth and egg whites in separate medium bowl; mix well. Stir into bread stuffing mixture. Cover; refrigerate 1 hour or until mixture is firm.

3. Preheat oven to 350°F. Shape mixture into 24 balls; place on ungreased baking sheet. Bake 15 minutes or until spinach balls are browned. Serve with mustard for dipping, if desired.

Makes 12 servings

Nutrients per Serving: 2 Spinach Balls

Calories 52	**Fiber** <1g
Fat 1g (sat <1g)	**Cholesterol** 1mg
Protein 3g	**Sodium** 227mg
Carbohydrate 9g	

Exchanges: 1/2 starch, 1/2 vegetable

Quick Pizza Snacks

Quick Pizza Snacks

meatless

Quick Recipe   *(Pictured above)*

3 English muffins, split and toasted
1 can (14-1/2 ounces) Italian-style diced tomatoes
3/4 cup shredded Italian cheese blend
Bell pepper strips (optional)

Preheat oven to 350°F. Place English muffin halves on ungreased baking sheet. Top each half with 1/4 cup tomatoes; sprinkle with 2 tablespoons cheese. Bake about 5 minutes or until cheese is melted and lightly browned. Garnish with bell pepper strips, if desired.

Makes 6 servings

Nutrients per Serving: 1 Pizza Snack

Calories 197	**Fiber** 1g
Fat 4g (sat 2g)	**Cholesterol** 10mg
Protein 7g	**Sodium** 489mg
Carbohydrate 19g	

Exchanges: 1 starch, 1 vegetable, 1 lean meat, 1 fat

Fruit Antipasto Platter

meatless

Quick Recipe   *(Pictured at right)*

> 2 cups DOLE® Fresh Pineapple, cut into wedges
> 2 medium, firm DOLE® Bananas, sliced diagonally
> 2 oranges, peeled and sliced
> 1/2 cup thinly sliced DOLE® Red Onion
> 1/2 pound low fat sharp Cheddar cheese, cut into 1-inch cubes
> 2 jars (6 ounces each) marinated artichoke hearts, drained and halved
> DOLE® Green or Red Leaf Lettuce
> 1/2 cup fat free or light Italian salad dressing

• Arrange fruit, onion, cheese and artichoke hearts on lettuce-lined platter; serve with dressing. Garnish, if desired.

Makes 10 servings

Nutrients per Serving: 1/10 of total recipe

Calories 128	**Fiber** 4g
Fat 4g (sat 1g)	**Cholesterol** 5mg
Protein 7g	**Sodium** 393mg
Carbohydrate 20g	

Exchanges: 1 fruit, 1 vegetable, 1 lean meat

Tip

A fresh pineapple will be fragrant and will yield slightly to the touch. Avoid pineapples with greenish tints, soft spots or fermented aromas.

Spicy Shrimp Cocktail

low carb

Quick Recipe

> 2 tablespoons olive or vegetable oil
> 1/4 cup finely chopped onion
> 1 tablespoon chopped green bell pepper
> 1 clove garlic, minced
> 1 can (8 ounces) CONTADINA® Tomato Sauce
> 1 tablespoon chopped pitted green olives, drained
> 1/4 teaspoon red pepper flakes
> 1 pound cooked shrimp, chilled

1. Heat oil in small skillet. Add onion, bell pepper and garlic; sauté until vegetables are tender. Stir in tomato sauce, olives and red pepper flakes.

2. Bring to a boil; simmer, uncovered, for 5 minutes. Cover.

3. Chill thoroughly. Combine sauce with shrimp in small bowl.   *Makes 6 servings*

Note: Serve over mixed greens, if desired.

Nutrients per Serving: 1/3 cup (without mixed greens)

Calories 129	**Fiber** 1g
Fat 6g (sat 1g)	**Cholesterol** 147mg
Protein 17g	**Sodium** 402mg
Carbohydrate 3g	

Exchanges: 1/2 vegetable, 2 lean meat

Fruit Antipasto Platter

Barbecued Meatballs

(Pictured at right)

2 pounds 95% lean ground beef
1-1/3 cups ketchup, divided
3 tablespoons seasoned dry bread crumbs
1 egg, lightly beaten
2 tablespoons dried onion flakes
3/4 teaspoon garlic salt
1/2 teaspoon black pepper
1 cup packed light brown sugar
1 can (6 ounces) tomato paste
1/4 cup cider vinegar
1/4 cup reduced-sodium soy sauce
1-1/2 teaspoons hot pepper sauce

Slow Cooker Directions

1. Preheat oven to 350°F. Combine ground beef, 1/3 cup ketchup, bread crumbs, egg, onion flakes, garlic salt and black pepper in medium bowl. Mix lightly, but thoroughly. Shape into 48 (1-inch) meatballs. Place meatballs in 2 (15×10-inch) jelly-roll pans or shallow roasting pans. Bake 18 minutes or until browned. Transfer meatballs to slow cooker.

2. Meanwhile, combine remaining 1 cup ketchup, brown sugar, tomato paste, vinegar, soy sauce and hot pepper sauce in medium bowl. Pour over meatballs. Cover; cook on LOW 4 hours. Serve with cocktail picks.

Makes 24 servings

Nutrients per Serving: 2 meatballs

Calories 106
Fat 2g (sat <1g)
Protein 8g
Carbohydrate 15g
Fiber 1g
Cholesterol 28mg
Sodium 352mg

Exchanges: 1 starch, 1 lean meat

Kiwi-on-a-Stick Appetizer

Quick Recipe

4 large kiwi fruit, peeled
1 small cucumber, washed, with ends removed
3 ounces prosciutto (6 thin slices), cut in half lengthwise
3 tablespoons lemon juice
1/4 teaspoon garlic powder
12 (5- or 6-inch) skewers

1. Score kiwi fruit and cucumber lengthwise with fork to decorate. Carefully cut each into slices of equal thickness. Kiwi should yield 6 slices each, cucumber 12 slices.

2. Stack one slice of cucumber in between two slices of kiwi fruit, matching diameter of slices. Carefully wrap each kiwi stack with a half-slice of prosciutto and mount diagonally on the tip of a skewer. Proceed with remaining skewers.

3. Brush all with combined lemon juice and garlic powder mixture and allow to chill, covered, until ready to serve.

Makes 6 servings (2 skewers per serving)

Favorite recipe from **Chilean Fresh Fruit Association**

Nutrients per Serving: 2 skewers

Calories 86
Fat 3g (sat 1g)
Protein 6g
Carbohydrate 11g
Fiber 2g
Cholesterol 15mg
Sodium 366mg

Exchanges: 1/2 fruit, 1/2 vegetable, 1/2 lean meat

Breads

‰ ‰ ‰

Tomato-Feta Focaccia

(Pictured at left)

1 package (16 ounces) frozen bread dough, thawed
2 fresh plum tomatoes, thinly sliced
1 cup crumbled feta cheese
1 tablespoon chopped fresh rosemary *or* 1 teaspoon dried
    rosemary, crushed

1. Spray 15×10-inch jelly-roll pan and hands with nonstick cooking spray. Fit dough into prepared pan, pressing gently to edges. (If dough won't stretch to edges of pan, let rest 5 minutes.) When dough is fully pressed into pan, cover with plastic wrap; let stand in warm place about 30 minutes or until doubled in bulk.

2. Preheat oven to 375°F. Arrange tomatoes in single layer over dough. Sprinkle with cheese and rosemary. Bake 23 to 25 minutes or until bottom is crisp and top is well browned. To further brown top, place in broiler 1 to 2 minutes.   *Makes 15 servings*

Nutrients per Serving: 1 (3×3-inch) piece

Calories 112	**Fiber** 1g
Fat 4g (sat 2g)	**Cholesterol** 9mg
Protein 5g	**Sodium** 280mg
Carbohydrate 16g	

Exchanges: 1 starch, 1/2 lean meat, 1/2 fat

Clockwise from top left: Blueberry Orange Muffins (page 39), Tomato-Feta Focaccia, Brunch-Time Zucchini-Date Bread (page 42) and Walnut-Cranberry Twist Danish (page 34)

Black Olive and Blue Cheese Bread Spirals

(Pictured at right)

1 package (11 ounces) refrigerated French bread dough

1/2 teaspoon dried oregano leaves

1/8 teaspoon dried red pepper flakes (optional)

1/3 cup chopped pitted black olives (about 12 large)

1/3 cup finely chopped green onions

1/4 cup finely chopped green bell pepper

1/4 cup crumbled blue cheese

1. Preheat oven to 350°F. Spray nonstick baking sheet with nonstick cooking spray; set aside.

2. Unroll bread dough on clean work surface. Sprinkle evenly with oregano and red pepper flakes, if desired. Top with olives, green onions and bell pepper. Sprinkle cheese over top. Roll up dough; gently transfer to prepared baking sheet.

3. Using serrated knife, cut 4 to 5 slits in loaf top. Bake 25 minutes or until deep golden in color. Remove bread to wire rack; cool completely. Lightly spray top of loaf with cooking spray. Cut into 11 slices to serve.

Makes 11 servings

Note: These spirals may be stored in an airtight container for up to 4 days.

Nutrients per Serving: 1 slice (1/11 of loaf)

Calories 89	**Fiber** 1g
Fat 2g (sat 1g)	**Cholesterol** 2mg
Protein 3g	**Sodium** 263mg
Carbohydrate 13g	

Exchanges: 1 starch

Cranberry Orange Bread

2 cups all-purpose flour

1 cup QUAKER® Oats (quick or old fashioned, uncooked)

1/4 cup granulated sugar *or* 2 tablespoons fructose

1 teaspoon baking powder

1/2 teaspoon baking soda

1/4 teaspoon salt (optional)

3/4 cup fat-free milk

3/4 cup egg substitute *or* 3 whole eggs

1/3 cup unsweetened orange juice

1/4 cup vegetable oil

1 tablespoon grated orange peel

1/2 cup chopped cranberries, fresh or frozen

1/4 cup chopped nuts* (optional)

*To toast nuts for extra flavor, spread evenly in small baking pan. Bake in 350°F oven 7 to 10 minutes or until light golden brown.

Heat oven to 350°F. Grease and flour 9×5-inch loaf pan. Combine flour, oats, granulated sugar, baking powder, baking soda and salt; mix well. Set aside. Beat milk, egg substitute, orange juice, vegetable oil and orange peel until thoroughly mixed. Add to dry ingredients, mixing just until moistened. Stir in cranberries and nuts. Pour into prepared pan. Bake 60 to 70 minutes or until wooden pick inserted into center comes out clean. Cool 10 minutes; remove from pan. Cool completely.

Makes 16 servings

Nutrients per Serving: 1 slice (1/16 of loaf)

Calories 136	**Fiber** 1g
Fat 4g (sat 1g)	**Cholesterol** <1mg
Protein 4g	**Sodium** 92mg
Carbohydrate 20g	

Exchanges: 1-1/2 starch, 1/2 fat

Black Olive and Blue Cheese Bread Spirals

Walnut-Cranberry Twist Danish

low fat

(Pictured on page 30)

**2-3/4 to 3-1/4 cups all-purpose flour, divided
1 package (1/4 ounce) active dry yeast
1/2 teaspoon ground allspice
3/4 cup fat-free milk
2 tablespoons granulated sugar
2 tablespoons butter
1 teaspoon salt
1 egg
1 cup chopped fresh or frozen
    cranberries, thawed
1/4 cup chopped walnuts
1/4 cup sugar substitute*
1 tablespoon powdered sugar**

*This recipe was tested with SPLENDA® Granular.

1. Combine 1 cup flour, yeast and allspice in large mixing bowl. Heat milk, granulated sugar, butter and salt to 120° to 130°F in small saucepan. Add milk mixture and egg to flour mixture. Beat with electric mixer at low speed 1 minute. Increase speed to high; beat 3 minutes. Stir in as much remaining flour as possible.

2. Turn dough out onto lightly floured surface. Knead about 3 to 5 minutes, adding enough remaining flour to make soft dough. Shape dough into ball. Place in bowl sprayed with nonstick cooking spray. Lightly spray dough surface with cooking spray. Cover loosely with plastic wrap. Let rise in warm place 1 to 1-1/2 hours or until doubled in bulk.

3. Meanwhile, combine cranberries, walnuts and sugar substitute in small bowl; set aside.

4. Punch down dough; cover and let rest 10 minutes. Lightly spray baking sheet with cooking spray; set aside.

5. On lightly floured surface, roll dough into 16×10-inch rectangle. Spread cranberry mixture over dough. Starting from long side, roll up dough into spiral log; pinch seam to seal. Place roll, seam side down, on floured surface. Cut roll in half lengthwise. On prepared baking sheet, loosely twist roll halves together, keeping cut sides up. Pinch ends to seal. Cover loosely with plastic wrap. Let rise in warm place about 30 minutes or until doubled in bulk.

6. Preheat oven to 350°F. Bake danish about 25 minutes or until light brown, covering with foil during last 5 minutes to prevent overbrowning. Remove from baking sheet. Cool completely. Sprinkle with powdered sugar.

Makes 16 servings

Nutrients per Serving: 1 (1-inch) piece

Calories 131	**Fiber** 1g
Fat 3g (sat 1g)	**Cholesterol** 17mg
Protein 4g	**Sodium** 159mg
Carbohydrate 24g	

Exchanges: 1-1/2 starch, 1/2 fat

Tip

Be sure to keep the cut sides of the roll halves facing up when you're twisting them together to make this danish. Not only will this ensure a nicer presentation, it will also keep the cranberries and walnuts from rolling off the dough.

Green Onion-Herb Crescent Rolls

Quick Recipe   *(Pictured below)*

1 can (8 ounces) refrigerated reduced-fat crescent roll dough
3 tablespoons minced green onions
1/2 teaspoon dried Italian seasoning

1. Preheat oven to 375°F. Separate dough into 8 triangles. Sprinkle about 1 teaspoon green onions over each triangle. Roll up loosely, starting at wide end of each triangle.

2. Place rolls on ungreased baking sheet; curve each into crescent shape. Sprinkle with Italian seasoning. Bake 10 to 12 minutes or until golden brown.   *Makes 8 servings*

Variation: Other herbs and spices can be used in place of the Italian seasoning. Chopped parsley, black pepper and sesame seeds are just a few of many flavorful substitutions to try.

Nutrients per Serving: 1 roll

Calories 102	**Fiber** <1g
Fat 5g (sat 1g)	**Cholesterol** 0mg
Protein 2g	**Sodium** 233mg
Carbohydrate 12g	

Exchanges: 1 starch, 1 fat

Green Onion-Herb Crescent Rolls

Raspberry Twist Ring

 low fat

(Pictured at right)

1/2 cup warm fat-free milk (105° to 115°F)
1/3 cup warm water (105° to 115°F)
1 package (1/4 ounce) active dry yeast
3 to 3-1/4 cups all-purpose flour, divided
3 tablespoons granulated sugar
1 egg
3 tablespoons butter, melted
1 teaspoon salt
1/4 cup reduced-sugar red raspberry
preserves
1 teaspoon grated orange peel
1/3 cup powdered sugar
2 teaspoons orange juice

1. Combine milk and water in large bowl. Dissolve yeast in mixture. Stir in 2-3/4 cups flour, granulated sugar, egg, butter and salt, stirring until soft dough forms.

2. Turn dough out onto lightly floured surface. Knead 5 to 8 minutes, adding enough remaining flour to make smooth and elastic dough. Place in bowl sprayed with nonstick cooking spray. Turn dough to coat surface with cooking spray. Cover loosely with plastic wrap. Let rise in warm place 45 to 60 minutes or until doubled in bulk.

3. Punch down dough. Cover and let rest in warm place 10 minutes.

4. Lightly spray baking sheet with cooking spray; set aside.

5. Roll dough into 16×9-inch rectangle on lightly floured surface. Combine preserves and orange peel in small bowl; spread over dough. Starting from long side, roll up dough into spiral log; pinch seam to seal. Form dough into ring on prepared baking sheet, keeping seam side down and pinching ends together to seal.

6. Use serrated knife to cut slices 3/4 of the way through dough at every inch. Slightly twist each section of dough out, forming many rings throughout ring. Loosely cover with plastic wrap. Let rise in warm place 30 to 45 minutes or until doubled in bulk.

7. Preheat oven to 350°F. Bake ring about 25 minutes or until light brown. Remove from baking sheet. Cool completely.

8. Combine powdered sugar and orange juice in small cup. Drizzle evenly over bread. Cut into 16 slices to serve. *Makes 16 servings*

Nutrients per Serving: 1 (1-1/4-inch) slice

Calories 142	**Fiber** 1g
Fat 3g (sat 1g)	**Cholesterol** 19mg
Protein 3g	**Sodium** 158mg
Carbohydrate 26g	

Exchanges: 1-1/2 starch, 1/2 fat

Tip

Are you looking for a warm place to let the dough rise? Place it inside a gas oven warmed by a pilot light, or in an electric oven heated to 200°F for one minute, then turned off.

Raspberry Twist Ring

Berry-Cheese Braid

Berry-Cheese Braid

(Pictured above)

Dough

    1 cup milk
    1 egg, lightly beaten
    3 tablespoons butter, softened
    1 teaspoon salt
    3 cups bread flour
    5 tablespoons sugar
    1-1/2 teaspoons active dry yeast

Filling and Topping

    1 package (8 ounces) reduced-fat cream
        cheese, softened
    1 egg
    1/4 cup plus 1 tablespoon sugar, divided
    1/2 teaspoon vanilla extract
    1 cup fresh raspberries
    1 cup fresh blueberries

Bread Machine Directions

1. Measuring carefully, place all dough ingredients in bread machine pan in order specified by owner's manual. Program dough cycle setting; press start. (Do not use delay cycle.)

2. For filling, beat cream cheese, egg, 1/4 cup sugar and vanilla in large bowl until well blended; set aside. Lightly spray 2 baking sheets with nonstick cooking spray; set aside.

3. When cycle is complete, remove dough to lightly floured surface. If necessary, knead in additional bread flour to make dough easy to handle. Divide dough in half. Roll each half into 12×9-inch* rectangle; carefully place rectangles on prepared baking sheets.

4. Spread filling lengthwise down center third of each dough rectangle, leaving 1-inch border at short ends. Sprinkle evenly with raspberries and blueberries. Fold 1-inch dough borders in toward centers. Make 5 cuts on each long side of dough rectangles, just up to filling, to form 6 strips on each side. Gently fold strips in toward centers, alternating left and right, and allowing some filling to show through. Sprinkle braids with remaining 1 tablespoon sugar. Cover with clean kitchen towels; let rise in warm, draft-free place 45 minutes or until doubled in size.

5. Preheat oven to 325°F. Bake braids 25 to 30 minutes or until golden brown. Remove from baking sheets; cool on wire racks. Serve at room temperature. Store in refrigerator. Refrigerate leftovers.   *Makes 24 servings (2 braids)*

For a slightly flatter appearance, roll each dough half into 14×9-inch rectangle.

Nutrients per Serving: 1 slice (1/24 of total recipe)

Calories 144	**Fiber** 1g
Fat 6g (sat 3g)	**Cholesterol** 33mg
Protein 4g	**Sodium** 152mg
Carbohydrate 19g	

Exchanges: 1-1/2 starch, 1 fat

Blueberry Orange Muffins

(Pictured on page 30)

1-3/4 cups all-purpose flour
1/3 cup sugar
2-1/2 teaspoons baking powder
1/2 teaspoon baking soda
1/2 teaspoon salt
1/2 teaspoon ground cinnamon
3/4 cup fat-free milk
1/4 cup butter, melted and slightly cooled
1 egg, lightly beaten
3 tablespoons frozen orange juice concentrate, thawed
1 teaspoon vanilla extract
3/4 cup fresh or frozen blueberries

1. Preheat oven to 400°F. Spray 12 standard (2-1/2-inch) muffin pan cups with nonstick cooking spray or line with paper baking cups.

2. Combine flour, sugar, baking powder, baking soda, salt and cinnamon in large bowl; set aside.

3. Beat milk, butter, egg, orange juice concentrate and vanilla in medium bowl with electric mixer at medium speed until well blended. Add milk mixture to dry ingredients. Mix lightly until dry ingredients are barely moistened (mixture will be lumpy). Add blueberries. Stir gently, just until berries are evenly distributed.

4. Fill prepared muffin cups 3/4 full. Bake 20 to 25 minutes (25 to 30 minutes if using frozen berries) or until wooden toothpick inserted into centers comes out clean. Cool in pan on wire rack 5 minutes. Remove from pan to wire rack. Serve warm. *Makes 12 servings*

Nutrients per Serving: 1 muffin

Calories 149	**Fiber** 1g
Fat 5g (sat 3g)	**Cholesterol** 29mg
Protein 3g	**Sodium** 307mg
Carbohydrate 24g	

Exchanges: 1 starch, 1/2 fruit, 1 fat

Caramelized Onion, Olive and Pesto Focaccia

1/4 cup prepared basil pesto
1 package (16 ounces) frozen bread dough, thawed
1 teaspoon olive oil
2 large sweet onions, sliced (about 3 cups)
1/4 teaspoon dried thyme leaves
1/4 teaspoon black pepper
1/8 teaspoon salt
6 pimiento-stuffed green olives, sliced (about 1/3 cup sliced)

1. Knead pesto into dough until evenly mixed throughout. Cover dough with plastic wrap; let rest 10 minutes.

2. Spray 15×10-inch jelly-roll pan and hands with nonstick cooking spray. Fit dough into prepared pan, pressing gently to edges. (If dough won't stretch to edges of pan, let rest 5 minutes.) When dough is fully pressed into pan, cover with plastic wrap; let stand in warm place about 30 minutes or until doubled in bulk.

3. Meanwhile, heat olive oil in large nonstick skillet over medium-high heat. Add onions; cook, stirring occasionally, about 20 minutes or until tender and well browned. Stir in thyme, pepper and salt.

4. Preheat oven to 375°F. Spread onions evenly over dough. Sprinkle with olives. Bake 20 minutes or until bottom is crisp and well browned. To further brown top, place in broiler 1 to 2 minutes.
Makes 15 servings

Nutrients per Serving: 1 (3×3-inch) piece

Calories 119	**Fiber** 1g
Fat 4g (sat <1g)	**Cholesterol** 1mg
Protein 4g	**Sodium** 257mg
Carbohydrate 18g	

Exchanges: 1 starch, 1/2 vegetable, 1/2 fat

Oat Bran Mini Bagels

3 to 3-1/2 cups all-purpose flour, divided
1 package (1/4 ounce) active dry yeast
2 tablespoons plus 1 teaspoon granulated sugar, divided
1 teaspoon salt
1-1/2 cups hot water (120° to 130°F)
1 cup uncooked oat bran
6 cups plus 1 tablespoon water, divided
1 egg white
1/4 cup uncooked old-fashioned oats

1. Combine 2 cups flour, yeast, 2 tablespoons sugar and salt in large bowl. Add 1-1/2 cups hot water. Beat 1 minute with electric mixer at low speed. Increase speed to high; beat 3 minutes.

2. Stir in oat bran and as much remaining flour as possible. Knead about 6 to 8 minutes, adding enough remaining flour to make moderately stiff dough. Cover loosely with plastic wrap. Let rest 10 minutes.

3. Lightly spray 2 baking sheets with nonstick cooking spray; set aside.

4. Divide dough into 24 equal portions. Shape each portion into ball. Press thumbs into center of each ball, stretching to form 1-1/2-inch hole. Place on prepared baking sheets. Cover loosely with plastic wrap. Let rise in warm place 30 minutes.

5. Preheat broiler. Broil bagels about 5 inches from heat 2 to 3 minutes, turning once. (Bagels should not brown.) Bring 6 cups water and remaining 1 teaspoon sugar to a boil in large Dutch oven. Drop bagels, 7 to 8 at a time, into boiling water mixture. Gently simmer 3 minutes, turning once. Drain on paper towels.

6. Meanwhile, preheat oven to 375°F. Spray baking sheets with cooking spray. Place boiled bagels on prepared sheets. Whisk together egg white and remaining 1 tablespoon water. Brush tops of bagels with egg white mixture. Sprinkle with oats. Bake about 20 minutes or until golden brown. *Makes 24 servings*

Nutrients per Serving: 1 (1-1/4-ounce) bagel

Calories 73	Fiber 1g
Fat <1g (sat <1g)	Cholesterol 0mg
Protein 2g	Sodium 112mg
Carbohydrate 15g	

Exchanges: 1 starch

❧ ❧ ❧

Whole Wheat Pumpkin Muffins

Quick Recipe

1-1/3 cups all-purpose flour
3/4 cup whole wheat flour
3 tablespoons sugar substitute*
1-1/2 teaspoons baking powder
1 teaspoon pumpkin pie spice
1/2 teaspoon *each* baking soda and salt
2 eggs, beaten
1 cup canned solid-pack pumpkin
2/3 cup orange juice
1/4 cup canola oil
3 tablespoons honey

*This recipe was tested with SPLENDA® Granular.

1. Preheat oven to 400°F. Spray 12 standard (2-1/2-inch) muffin pan cups with nonstick cooking spray or line with paper baking cups.

2. Combine flours, sugar substitute, baking powder, pumpkin pie spice, baking soda and salt in large bowl. Combine eggs, pumpkin, orange juice, oil and honey in medium bowl. Add to dry ingredients; stir just until moistened.

3. Spoon batter into prepared muffin cups. Bake 15 to 20 minutes or until wooden toothpick inserted into centers comes out clean. Cool in pan on wire rack 5 minutes. Remove from pan to wire rack. Serve warm. *Makes 12 servings*

Nutrients per Serving: 1 muffin

Calories 164	Fiber 2g
Fat 6g (sat 1g)	Cholesterol 35mg
Protein 4g	Sodium 214mg
Carbohydrate 26g	

Exchanges: 1-1/2 starch, 1 fat

Onion-Wheat Pan Bread

(Pictured below)

1/3 cup wheat germ, divided
1-3/4 cups all-purpose flour
2 tablespoons sugar
1-3/4 teaspoons baking powder
1/2 teaspoon salt
1 cup 2% milk
1/3 cup finely chopped green onions
1/3 cup canola oil
1 egg
2 tablespoons grated Parmesan cheese
1 tablespoon toasted sesame seeds

1. Preheat oven to 400°F. Spray 9-inch cast iron skillet with nonstick cooking spray.* Heat skillet in oven 5 minutes. Reserve 1 tablespoon wheat germ.

2. Combine remaining wheat germ, flour, sugar, baking powder and salt in large bowl. Beat milk, onions, oil and egg in medium bowl with fork. Add to flour mixture; stir just until moistened. Spoon into preheated skillet. Sprinkle with reserved 1 tablespoon wheat germ, cheese and sesame seeds.

3. Bake 15 minutes or until golden brown and wooden toothpick inserted into center comes out clean. Cool in skillet on wire rack 15 minutes. Serve warm. *Makes 12 servings*

Or, substitute 9-inch round pan sprayed with nonstick cooking spray. Do not preheat pan in oven. Increase baking time 5 minutes, for a total of 20 minutes.

Nutrients per Serving: 1 wedge (1/12 of loaf)

Calories 165	**Fiber** 1g
Fat 8g (sat 1g)	**Cholesterol** 20mg
Protein 4g	**Sodium** 198mg
Carbohydrate 19g	

Exchanges: 1-1/2 starch, 1-1/2 fat

Onion-Wheat Pan Bread

Brunch-Time Zucchini-Date Bread

low fat

(Pictured on page 30)

Bread

- 1 cup chopped pitted dates
- 1 cup water
- 1 cup whole wheat flour
- 1 cup all-purpose flour
- 2 tablespoons granulated sugar
- 1 teaspoon baking powder
- 1/2 teaspoon *each* baking soda, salt and ground cinnamon
- 1/4 teaspoon ground cloves
- 2 eggs
- 1 cup shredded zucchini, pressed dry with paper towels

Cream Cheese Spread

- 1 package (8 ounces) fat-free cream cheese
- 1/4 cup powdered sugar
- 1 tablespoon vanilla extract
- 1/8 teaspoon ground cinnamon
- Dash ground cloves

1. Preheat oven to 350°F. Spray 8×4×2-inch loaf pan with nonstick cooking spray; set aside.

2. For bread, combine dates and water in small saucepan. Bring to a boil over medium-high heat. Remove from heat; let stand 15 minutes. Combine flours, granulated sugar, baking powder, baking soda, salt, cinnamon and cloves in large bowl. Beat eggs in medium bowl; stir in date mixture and zucchini. Stir egg mixture into flour mixture just until dry ingredients are moistened. Pour batter evenly into prepared pan. Bake 30 to 35 minutes or until wooden toothpick inserted into center comes out clean. Cool 5 minutes. Remove from pan. Cool completely on wire rack.

3. Meanwhile, for cream cheese spread, combine cream cheese, powdered sugar, vanilla, cinnamon and cloves in small bowl. Beat until smooth. Cover and refrigerate until ready to use.

4. Cut bread into 16 slices. Serve with cream cheese spread.　　*Makes 16 servings*

Nutrients per Serving: 1 slice (1/16 of loaf) with about 1 tablespoon spread

Calories 124	Fiber 2g
Fat 1g (sat <1g)	Cholesterol 27mg
Protein 5g	Sodium 260mg
Carbohydrate 24g	

Exchanges: 1 starch, 1/2 fruit, 1/2 lean meat

ɚ ɚ ɚ

Potato Dill Biscuits

- 1 medium COLORADO potato, peeled and chopped
- 1/2 cup water
- 2 cups all-purpose flour
- 1 tablespoon baking powder
- 2 teaspoons sugar
- 1 teaspoon dried dill weed
- 1/2 teaspoon cream of tartar
- 1/2 teaspoon salt
- 1/4 cup shortening
- 1/4 cup cold butter

In small saucepan combine chopped potato and 1/2 cup water. Cover and cook over medium heat about 10 minutes or until potato is tender. *Do not drain.* Mash until smooth or place mixture in blender and blend until smooth. Add additional water to measure 1 cup. In mixing bowl combine flour, baking powder, sugar, dill, cream of tartar and salt. Cut in shortening and butter until mixture resembles coarse crumbs. Add potato mixture. Stir just until mixture clings together. On lightly floured surface, knead dough 10 or 12 strokes. Pat or roll into 8-inch square. Cut into 16 squares. Place biscuits on baking sheet. Bake in 450°F oven 10 to 12 minutes or until lightly browned. Serve warm.　　*Makes 16 biscuits*

Favorite recipe from **Colorado Potato Administrative Committee**

Nutrients per Serving: 1 biscuit

Calories 121	Fiber 1g
Fat 6g (sat 3g)	Cholesterol 8mg
Protein 2g	Sodium 188mg
Carbohydrate 14g	

Exchanges: 1 starch, 1-1/2 fat

Ham and Cheese Corn Muffins

Ham and Cheese Corn Muffins

Quick Recipe   *(Pictured above)*

  1 package (about 8 ounces) corn muffin
    mix
1/2 cup chopped extra-lean deli ham
1/2 cup shredded reduced-fat Swiss cheese
1/3 cup 2% milk
  1 egg
  1 tablespoon Dijon mustard

1. Preheat oven to 400°F. Spray 9 (2-3/4-inch) muffin cups with nonstick cooking spray or line with paper baking cups; set aside.

2. Combine muffin mix, ham and cheese in medium bowl. Beat milk, egg and mustard in 1-cup glass measure. Stir milk mixture into dry ingredients; mix just until moistened.

3. Fill prepared muffin cups 2/3 full. Bake 18 to 20 minutes or until light golden brown. Cool 5 minutes in pan on wire rack. Remove from pan. Serve warm.   *Makes 9 muffins*

Serving Suggestion: Serve Ham and Cheese Corn Muffins with honey-flavored butter, prepared by combining equal amounts of honey and softened butter.

Nutrients per Serving: 1 muffin (without honey-flavored butter)

Calories 150	**Fiber** 2g
Fat 6g (sat 2g)	**Cholesterol** 33mg
Protein 6g	**Sodium** 411mg
Carbohydrate 18g	

Exchanges: 1 starch, 1 lean meat, 1/2 fat

ঞ ঞ ঞ

Festive Cornmeal Biscuits

low fat

Quick Recipe

1-3/4 cups all-purpose flour
1/2 cup yellow cornmeal
  1 tablespoon baking powder
  1 tablespoon sugar
  1 teaspoon salt
1/4 teaspoon baking soda
  3 tablespoons cold butter
3/4 cup buttermilk
  1 egg white, beaten
    Reduced-sugar peach or strawberry
      preserves (optional)

1. Preheat oven to 425°F. Combine flour, cornmeal, baking powder, sugar, salt and baking soda in large bowl; mix well. Cut in butter with pastry blender or two knives until mixture forms coarse crumbs. Add buttermilk; mix just until dough holds together.

2. Turn dough out onto lightly floured surface; knead 8 to 10 times. Pat dough to 1/2-inch thickness; cut with decorative 2-inch cookie or biscuit cutter. Spray baking sheet with nonstick cooking spray. Place biscuits on sheet. Brush tops lightly with beaten egg white. Bake 12 to 13 minutes or until light golden brown. Serve with preserves, if desired.   *Makes 12 servings*

Nutrients per Serving: 1 biscuit

Calories 122	**Fiber** 1g
Fat 3g (sat 2g)	**Cholesterol** 9mg
Protein 3g	**Sodium** 339mg
Carbohydrate 20g	

Exchanges: 1-1/2 starch, 1/2 fat

Orange Chocolate Chip Bread

(Pictured at right)

1/2 cup nonfat milk
1/2 cup plain nonfat yogurt
1/3 cup sugar
1/4 cup orange juice
1 egg, slightly beaten
1 tablespoon freshly grated orange peel
3 cups all-purpose biscuit baking mix
1/2 cup HERSHEY'S MINI CHIPS™ Semi-Sweet Chocolate Chips

1. Heat oven to 350°F. Grease 9×5×3-inch loaf pan or spray with vegetable cooking spray.

2. Stir together milk, yogurt, sugar, orange juice, egg and orange peel in large bowl; add baking mix. With spoon, beat until well blended, about 1 minute. Stir in small chocolate chips. Pour into prepared pan.

3. Bake 45 to 50 minutes or until wooden pick inserted into center comes out clean. Cool 10 minutes; remove from pan to wire rack. Cool completely before slicing. Garnish as desired. Wrap leftover bread in foil or plastic wrap. Store at room temperature, or freeze for longer storage.   *Makes 1 loaf (16 slices)*

Nutrients per Serving: 1 slice (1/16 of loaf)

Calories 150	Fiber 1g
Fat 5g (sat 2g)	Cholesterol 15mg
Protein 3g	Sodium 280mg
Carbohydrate 23g	

Exchanges: 1-1/2 starch, 1/2 fat

Potato Parmesan Muffins

1 medium COLORADO potato, peeled and coarsely chopped
1/2 cup water
1/4 cup milk
1-2/3 cups all-purpose flour
3 tablespoons sugar
2 tablespoons grated Parmesan cheese, divided
2 teaspoons baking powder
1/2 teaspoon dried basil leaves
1/4 teaspoon baking soda
1/4 cup vegetable oil
1 egg, beaten

In small saucepan cook potato in 1/2 cup water, covered, over medium heat about 10 minutes or until tender. *Do not drain.* Mash until smooth, or place mixture in blender container and blend until smooth. Add enough milk to measure 1 cup. In mixing bowl combine flour, sugar, cheese, baking powder, basil and baking soda. Mix well. Combine potato mixture, oil and beaten egg; add all at once to flour mixture. Stir just until moistened. Spoon into greased or paper-lined muffin cups. Bake at 400°F for 20 minutes or until lightly browned. Remove from pan and cool on wire rack.

Makes 10 muffins

Favorite recipe from **Colorado Potato Administrative Committee**

Nutrients per Serving: 1 muffin

Calories 170	Fiber 1g
Fat 7g (sat 1g)	Cholesterol 23mg
Protein 4g	Sodium 174mg
Carbohydrate 23g	

Exchanges: 1-1/2 starch, 1 fat

Bran and Honey Rye Breadsticks

Bran and Honey Rye Breadsticks

 low fat low sodium

(Pictured above)

1 package (1/4 ounce) active dry yeast
1 teaspoon sugar
1-1/2 cups warm water (110°F)
3-3/4 cups all-purpose flour, divided
1 tablespoon canola oil
1 tablespoon honey
1/2 teaspoon salt
1 cup rye flour
1/2 cup uncooked whole bran cereal
1/2 cup fat-free milk

1. Combine yeast, sugar and warm water in large bowl. Let stand 5 minutes or until bubbly. Add 1 cup all-purpose flour, oil, honey and salt. Beat with electric mixer at medium speed 3 minutes. Stir in rye flour, bran cereal and 2 cups all-purpose flour (or enough to make moderately stiff dough).

2. Turn dough out onto lightly floured surface. Knead about 10 minutes, adding enough remaining flour to make a smooth and elastic dough. Place in bowl sprayed with nonstick cooking spray; turn dough to coat surface with cooking spray. Cover with damp kitchen cloth; let rise in warm place 40 to 45 minutes or until doubled in bulk.

3. Spray 2 baking sheets with cooking spray. Punch down dough. Divide into 24 equal-size pieces on lightly floured surface. Roll each piece into 8-inch rope. Place on prepared baking sheets. Cover and let rise in warm place 30 to 35 minutes or until doubled in bulk.

4. Preheat oven to 375°F. Brush breadsticks with milk. Bake 18 to 20 minutes or until breadsticks are golden brown. Remove from baking sheets. Cool on wire racks.   *Makes 24 breadsticks*

Nutrients per Serving: 1 breadstick

Calories 104	**Fiber** 1g
Fat 1g (sat <1g)	**Cholesterol** <1mg
Protein 3g	**Sodium** 53mg
Carbohydrate 21g	

Exchanges: 1-1/2 starch

Tip

Remember to only lightly dust your work surface with flour. Too much flour will make your baked goods dry, dense and heavy.

Strawberry-Filled Muffins

2 cups all-purpose flour
1/4 cup sugar substitute*
3 tablespoons sugar
1-1/2 teaspoons baking powder
3/4 teaspoon ground allspice
1/4 teaspoon baking soda
1/4 teaspoon salt
3/4 cup fat-free buttermilk
1/3 cup egg substitute
3 tablespoons canola oil
1/4 cup sugar-free strawberry or raspberry fruit spread
1/4 cup slivered almonds, toasted

*This recipe was tested with SPLENDA® Granular.

1. Preheat oven to 400°F. Spray 12 standard (2-1/2-inch) muffin pan cups with nonstick cooking spray or line with paper baking cups; set aside.

2. Combine flour, sugar substitute, sugar, baking powder, allspice, baking soda and salt in medium bowl. Make well in center of mixture.

3. Combine buttermilk, egg substitute and oil in small bowl. Add to well in flour mixture, stirring just until moistened.

4. Spoon batter into prepared muffin cups, filling each about 1/4 full. Spoon 1 teaspoon fruit spread into center of each. Spoon remaining batter on top of fruit spread. Sprinkle with almonds. Bake 18 to 20 minutes or until golden. Cool in pan on wire rack 5 minutes. Remove muffins to wire rack. Serve warm. *Makes 12 servings*

Nutrients per Serving: 1 muffin

Calories 158	**Fiber** 1g
Fat 5g (sat <1g)	**Cholesterol** 1mg
Protein 4g	**Sodium** 165mg
Carbohydrate 24g	

Exchanges: 1-1/2 starch, 1 fat

Trade Wind Muffins

1/2 cup sliced almonds
2 cups sifted all-purpose flour
1 teaspoon baking soda
1 teaspoon salt
1 cup granulated sugar
3 ounces cream cheese, at room temperature
2 teaspoons vanilla
1 egg, beaten
1/2 cup cultured sour cream
1 (20-ounce) can crushed pineapple, drained, juice reserved

Glaze (optional)
1 cup powdered sugar
1 tablespoon margarine
1 tablespoon reserved pineapple juice

Grease muffin pans and sprinkle with almonds.

Sift flour with baking soda and salt. Beat granulated sugar, cream cheese and vanilla together until smooth. Blend in egg. Add flour mixture alternately with sour cream. Fold in drained pineapple. Spoon into prepared pans.

Bake at 350°F for 35 minutes or until done. Let stand in pan 5 to 10 minutes. Turn out onto wire rack. For glaze, whisk together powdered sugar, margarine and pineapple juice. Spread muffins with glaze, if desired. *Makes 18 muffins*

Favorite recipe from **North Dakota Wheat Commission**

Nutrients per Serving: 1 muffin without glaze

Calories 151	**Fiber** 1g
Fat 5g (sat 2g)	**Cholesterol** 20mg
Protein 3g	**Sodium** 186mg
Carbohydrate 25g	

Exchanges: 1 starch, 1/2 fruit, 1 fat

Breakfast & Brunch

≥ ≥ ≥

Very Berry Raspberry Yogurt Parfaits

low fat   low sodium

Quick Recipe   *(Pictured at left)*

>   3 cups plain fat-free yogurt
>   2 tablespoons sugar-free raspberry preserves
>   2 teaspoons sugar substitute*
>   1/2 teaspoon vanilla extract
>   2 cups sliced strawberries
>   1 cup fresh or thawed frozen blueberries
>   4 tablespoons sliced almonds, toasted

This recipe was tested with SPLENDA® Granular.

1. Combine yogurt, preserves, sugar substitute and vanilla in medium bowl.

2. Layer 1/2 cup yogurt mixture, 1/4 cup strawberries and 1/4 cup blueberries in each of 4 parfait glasses. Layer 1/4 cup yogurt mixture and 1/4 cup strawberries over blueberry layer in each glass. Sprinkle each parfait with 1 tablespoon almonds. Serve immediately.   *Makes 4 servings*

Nutrients per Serving: 1 parfait

Calories 179	**Fiber** 3g
Fat 3g (sat <1g)	**Cholesterol** 4mg
Protein 10g	**Sodium** 104mg
Carbohydrate 33g	

Exchanges: 1-1/2 fruit, 1 milk

Clockwise from top left: *Biscuit Pizzas (page 50), Blueberry Walnut Coffee Cake (page 52), French Toast with Warm Apples (page 56) and Very Berry Raspberry Yogurt Parfaits*

Biscuit Pizzas

(Pictured on page 48)

> 1 package (16 ounces) refrigerated flaky biscuits
> 8 tablespoons tomato sauce
> 2 slices bacon
> 1/4 cup chopped green bell pepper
> 1/4 cup chopped onion
> 1-1/4 cups egg substitute
> 1/4 teaspoon black pepper
> 1/2 cup shredded reduced-fat Cheddar cheese

1. Preheat oven to 375°F. Place biscuits 2 inches apart on large ungreased baking sheet. Make indentation in center of each biscuit to form edge. Spoon 1 tablespoon tomato sauce into center of each biscuit. Set aside.

2. Spray large nonstick skillet with nonstick cooking spray. Cook bacon, bell pepper and onion over medium-high heat until bacon is crisp, stirring occasionally. Remove bacon to paper towels. Remove vegetables. Drain fat from skillet.

3. Spray same skillet with cooking spray. Return vegetables to skillet. Add egg substitute. Season with black pepper. Cook over medium heat, stirring often, about 1 minute or until eggs are cooked through.

4. Divide egg mixture among biscuit centers. Crumble bacon; sprinkle over egg mixture. Top with cheese. Bake 15 to 17 minutes or until pizza edges are golden brown.   *Makes 8 servings*

Variation: Try substituting reduced-fat sausage for the bacon in this recipe. Or, try another of your favorite reduced-fat cheeses in place of the Cheddar.

Nutrients per Serving: 1 pizza

Calories 226	**Fiber** <1g
Fat 10g (sat 2g)	**Cholesterol** 3mg
Protein 11g	**Sodium** 814mg
Carbohydrate 25g	

Exchanges: 1-1/2 starch, 1/2 vegetable, 1 lean meat, 1-1/2 fat

Raspberry Puffs

Quick Recipe

> 1 package (8 ounces) refrigerated reduced-fat crescent roll dough
> 1/4 cup reduced-sugar raspberry fruit spread
> 1/2 (8-ounce) package reduced-fat cream cheese
> 2 tablespoons fat-free milk
> 2 to 3 teaspoons sugar substitute*
> 1/4 teaspoon vanilla extract

*This recipe was tested with SPLENDA® Granular.

1. Preheat oven to 400°F.

2. Separate crescent roll dough into 8 triangles; unroll on lightly floured surface. Brush 1-1/2 teaspoons fruit spread evenly over each triangle. Roll up each triangle, starting at wide end. Place crescents on ungreased baking sheet. Bake according to package directions.

3. Meanwhile, combine cream cheese, milk, sugar substitute and vanilla in small bowl; beat with electric mixer at medium speed until smooth. Spoon about 1 tablespoon cream cheese mixture over each cooled puff.
Makes 10 servings

Variation: For an even lighter tasting roll, replace the cream cheese mixture with powdered sugar. Simply sprinkle 2 tablespoons evenly over all.

Nutrients per Serving: 1 Puff

Calories 127	**Fiber** 0g
Fat 6g (sat 2g)	**Cholesterol** 6mg
Protein 3g	**Sodium** 223mg
Carbohydrate 16g	

Exchanges: 1 starch, 1 fat

Breakfast Pizza Margherita

Quick Recipe

- 1 (12-inch) Italian bread shell
- 3 slices bacon
- 1 container (16 ounces) egg substitute
- 1/2 cup fat-free milk
- 1 tablespoon plus 1-1/2 teaspoons chopped fresh basil, divided
- 1/8 teaspoon black pepper
- 2 fresh plum tomatoes, thinly sliced
- 1/2 cup shredded reduced-fat mozzarella cheese
- 1/4 cup shredded reduced-fat Cheddar cheese

1. Preheat oven to 450°F. Place bread shell on 12-inch pizza pan. Bake 6 to 8 minutes or until heated through.

2. Spray large nonstick skillet with nonstick cooking spray. Brown bacon over medium-high heat. Remove from skillet; set aside. Drain fat. Crumble bacon when cool.

3. Combine egg substitute, milk, 1-1/2 teaspoons basil and pepper in medium bowl. Spray same large nonstick skillet with cooking spray. Add egg substitute mixture to skillet. Cook over medium heat until mixture begins to set around edge. Gently stir eggs, allowing uncooked portion to flow underneath. Repeat gentle stirring of eggs every 1 to 2 minutes or until just set. Remove from heat.

4. Arrange tomato slices on warmed bread shell. Spoon scrambled eggs over top. Sprinkle with bacon. Top with cheeses. Return to hot oven about 1 minute more or until cheese melts. Sprinkle with remaining 1 tablespoon basil. Cut into 6 wedges. Serve immediately.

Makes 6 servings

Nutrients per Serving: 1 wedge

Calories 310	**Fiber** 2g
Fat 9g (sat 2g)	**Cholesterol** 8mg
Protein 21g	**Sodium** 660mg
Carbohydrate 35g	

Exchanges: 2 starch, 1/2 vegetable, 2 lean meat, 1 fat

Strawberry-Topped Waffles with Sweet and Creamy Sauce

Quick Recipe   (Pictured below)

- 3 ounces reduced-fat cream cheese
- 1/4 cup fat-free half-and-half
- 2 tablespoons sugar substitute*
- 1/4 teaspoon vanilla extract
- 4 frozen waffles
- 1 cup sliced fresh strawberries

*This recipe was tested with SPLENDA® Granular.

1. Combine cream cheese, half-and-half, sugar substitute and vanilla in blender container; cover and blend until smooth.

2. Toast waffles. Spoon sauce over waffles. Top with strawberries. *Makes 4 servings*

Nutrients per Serving: 1 waffle with 2 tablespoons sauce and 1/4 cup strawberries

Calories 160	**Fiber** 2g
Fat 7g (sat 3g)	**Cholesterol** 15mg
Protein 5g	**Sodium** 390mg
Carbohydrate 20g	

Exchanges: 1 starch. 1/2 fruit, 1 fat

Strawberry-Topped Waffle with Sweet and Creamy Sauce

French Toast with Warm Apples

Quick Recipe (Pictured on page 48)

4 egg whites
2 eggs
3 tablespoons sugar substitute,* divided
3 tablespoons fat-free milk
1/2 teaspoon vanilla extract, divided
1/8 teaspoon ground nutmeg
4 (1-ounce) slices Italian bread
2 teaspoons canola oil
1 cup sliced unpeeled apples
2 tablespoons water
1 tablespoon reduced-fat butter
4 teaspoons sugar-free pancake syrup

This recipe was tested with SPLENDA® Granular.

1. Place egg whites, eggs, 2 tablespoons sugar substitute, milk, 1/4 teaspoon vanilla and nutmeg in 13×9-inch baking dish; stir with fork until well blended. Add bread slices; turn several times to coat evenly.

2. Heat oil in medium nonstick skillet over medium heat until hot. Tilt skillet to coat with oil. Add bread slices; cook 3 minutes. Turn; cook 3 minutes longer or until golden.

3. Meanwhile, add apples, water, and remaining 1 tablespoon sugar substitute to small saucepan. Bring to a boil over medium heat. Reduce heat; simmer, uncovered, 2 minutes or until apples are just crisp-tender. Remove from heat. Stir in butter and remaining 1/4 teaspoon vanilla.

4. Top each toast slice with 1 teaspoon syrup and 1/4 cup apple mixture.

Makes 4 servings

Nutrients per Serving: 1 slice French toast with 1 teaspoon syrup and 1/4 cup apple mixture

Calories 197	**Fiber** 1g
Fat 8g (sat 2g)	**Cholesterol** 110mg
Protein 10g	**Sodium** 304mg
Carbohydrate 27g	

Exchanges: 2 starch, 1 lean meat, 1 fat

Fruit-Filled Puff Pancake

Quick Recipe

1 tablespoon butter
1/2 cup all-purpose flour
1/4 teaspoon salt
2 eggs
1/2 cup fat-free milk
1 teaspoon vanilla extract
2 cups sliced fresh strawberries
1 teaspoon sugar substitute*
2 teaspoons powdered sugar

This recipe was tested with SPLENDA® Granular.

1. Preheat oven to 400°F.

2. Place butter in 9-inch glass pie plate. Place in oven 2 minutes or until butter is bubbly. Swirl plate to coat bottom and side.

3. Meanwhile, combine flour and salt in large bowl. Whisk eggs in medium bowl until frothy. Add milk and vanilla to eggs; whisk until blended. Add egg mixture to flour mixture; whisk until blended. (Batter will be slightly lumpy.)

4. Add melted butter to batter; mix well. Pour batter into hot pie plate. Bake 20 minutes or until pancake is puffed and lightly browned.

5. Meanwhile, combine strawberries and sugar substitute in medium bowl.

6. Cut puff into 4 wedges to serve. Spoon fruit over hot pancake wedges. Sprinkle with powdered sugar. Serve immediately.

Makes 4 servings

Nutrients per Serving: 1 wedge with 1/2 cup strawberries

Calories 166	**Fiber** 2g
Fat 6g (sat 3g)	**Cholesterol** 114mg
Protein 7g	**Sodium** 202mg
Carbohydrate 22g	

Exchanges: 1 starch, 1/2 fruit, 1/2 lean meat, 1 fat

Vegetable Omelet

Vegetable Omelet

meatless

Quick Recipe   *(Pictured above)*

        Ratatouille (recipe follows)
    5 eggs
    6 egg whites *or* 3/4 cup egg substitute
    1/4 cup fat-free milk
    1/2 teaspoon salt
    1/8 teaspoon black pepper
    4 (1-ounce) slices Italian bread
    2 cloves garlic, halved

1. Prepare Ratatouille; keep warm.

2. Spray 12-inch nonstick skillet with nonstick cooking spray; heat over medium heat. Beat eggs, egg whites, milk, salt and pepper in large bowl until foamy. Pour egg mixture into skillet; cook over medium-high heat 2 to 3 minutes or until bottom of omelet is set. Reduce heat to medium-low. Cover; cook 8 minutes or until top of omelet is set. Remove from heat.

3. Spoon half of Ratatouille down center of omelet. Carefully fold omelet in half; slide onto serving plate. Spoon remaining Ratatouille over top of omelet.

4. Toast bread slices. Rub both sides of warm toast with cut garlic cloves. Serve omelet with toast and fresh fruit, if desired.

Makes 4 servings

Ratatouille

    1 cup chopped onion
    1/2 cup chopped green bell pepper
    2 cloves garlic, minced
    4 cups cubed unpeeled eggplant
    1 medium yellow summer squash, sliced
    1 cup chopped fresh tomatoes
    1/4 cup finely chopped fresh basil *or*
        1 teaspoon dried basil leaves
    1 tablespoon finely chopped fresh
        oregano *or* 1 teaspoon dried oregano
        leaves
    2 teaspoons finely chopped fresh thyme
        ***or* 1/2 teaspoon dried thyme leaves**

Spray large skillet with nonstick cooking spray; heat over medium heat. Add onion, bell pepper and garlic; cook and stir 5 minutes or until tender. Add eggplant, summer squash, tomatoes, basil, oregano and thyme. Cover; cook over medium heat 8 to 10 minutes or until vegetables are tender. Uncover; cook 2 to 3 minutes or until all liquid is absorbed.   *Makes about 4 cups*

Hint: Fresh eggplant is available year-round. When purchasing an eggplant, look for one that is plump, glossy and heavy. Avoid any with scarred, bruised or dull surfaces.

Nutrients per Serving: 1/4 of omelet with about 1 cup Ratatouille and 1 toast slice (without fruit)

Calories 274	**Fiber** 2g
Fat 8g (sat 2g)	**Cholesterol** 266mg
Protein 19g	**Sodium** 620mg
Carbohydrate 32g	

Exchanges: 1 starch, 3 vegetable, 2 lean meat, 1/2 fat

Banana-Pineapple Breakfast Shake

Quick Recipe   *(Pictured at right)*

- 2 cups plain fat-free yogurt
- 1 can (8 ounces) crushed pineapple in juice, undrained
- 1 medium ripe banana
- 5 tablespoons plus 1 teaspoon sugar substitute*
- 1 cup ice cubes
- 1 teaspoon vanilla extract
- 1/8 teaspoon ground nutmeg

This recipe was tested with SPLENDA® Granular.

Place all ingredients in blender; cover and blend until smooth. Pour into 4 serving glasses.

Makes 4 servings

Hint: This recipe is perfect for a party or any other special occasion. Just increase the ingredient amounts, so you'll have enough for everyone to enjoy!

Nutrients per Serving: 1 cup shake

Calories 140	**Fiber** 1g
Fat <1g (sat <1g)	**Cholesterol** 2mg
Protein 8g	**Sodium** 95mg
Carbohydrate 27g	

Exchanges: 1/2 starch, 1 fruit, 1/2 milk

Tip

One packet of sugar substitute is typically equal to two teaspoons of spoonable sugar substitute.

Lemon Poppy Seed Waffles with Fresh Blueberries

- 1-1/2 cups fresh or thawed frozen blueberries
- 1/2 cup plus 1 teaspoon sugar substitute,* divided
- 3/4 cup all-purpose flour
- 1/3 cup whole wheat flour
- 2 teaspoons poppy seeds
- 1/2 teaspoon baking powder
- 1/4 teaspoon baking soda
- 1/8 teaspoon salt
- 3/4 cup egg substitute
- 1/2 cup 1% buttermilk
- 1 tablespoon canola oil
- 1 teaspoon grated lemon peel
- 1/2 teaspoon vanilla extract
- 1 teaspoon powdered sugar

This recipe was tested with SPLENDA® Granular.

1. Combine blueberries and 1 teaspoon sugar substitute in small microwavable bowl. Microwave at MEDIUM (50%) 3 to 4 minutes or until warm. Set aside.

2. Combine flours, remaining 1/2 cup sugar substitute, poppy seeds, baking powder, baking soda and salt in medium bowl. Combine egg substitute, buttermilk, oil, lemon peel and vanilla in another medium bowl. Add liquid mixture to flour mixture; stir just until moistened.

3. Spray waffle iron with nonstick cooking spray; preheat. Spoon 1/4 cup batter into iron; spread to edges. Cook 4 to 5 minutes or until steaming stops. Repeat with remaining batter. Sprinkle cooked waffles with powdered sugar. Serve with blueberry sauce.

Makes 6 servings

Nutrients per Serving: 1 (4-inch) waffle with 1/4 cup blueberries

Calories 171	**Fiber** 2g
Fat 4g (sat 1g)	**Cholesterol** 1mg
Protein 7g	**Sodium** 213mg
Carbohydrate 26g	

Exchanges: 1-1/2 starch, 1/2 fruit, 1/2 lean meat

Banana-Pineapple Breakfast Shake

Cornmeal, Sausage and Chile Casserole

**1/4 pound uncooked turkey sausage
 breakfast links**
1 medium red bell pepper, diced
1/2 cup diced onion
1 teaspoon ground cumin
1/2 to 1 teaspoon chili powder
**1 cup fat-free reduced-sodium chicken
 broth**
1/2 cup uncooked yellow cornmeal
3 egg whites
**1 can (about 4 ounces) diced mild green
 chilies, drained**
**1/2 cup shredded reduced-fat Cheddar
 cheese**
3 eggs, beaten
3/4 cup prepared salsa

1. Heat large nonstick skillet over medium-high heat. Remove sausage casings. Add sausage, bell pepper and onion to skillet. Cook, breaking up sausage, about 5 minutes or until sausage is no longer pink and vegetables are crisp-tender. Stir in cumin and chili powder; cook 1 minute.

2. Add chicken broth to skillet; bring to a boil. Gradually add cornmeal; cook 1 minute, stirring constantly to break up any lumps. Transfer mixture to large bowl; set aside to cool slightly.

3. Preheat oven to 375°F. Spray 11×7-inch glass baking dish with nonstick cooking spray; set aside.

4. Meanwhile, beat egg whites in medium bowl with electric mixer at high speed until stiff peaks form.

5. Stir chilies and cheese into cornmeal mixture. Add whole eggs; stir to combine. Gently stir 1/4 of beaten egg white into cornmeal mixture. Fold in remaining egg white. Spoon mixture into prepared dish. Bake 30 minutes or until center is set and edges are lightly browned. Remove from oven. Cool slightly. Cut into 6 pieces. Serve immediately with salsa.

Makes 6 servings

Nutrients per Serving: 1 piece with 2 tablespoons salsa

Calories 160	**Fiber** 2g
Fat 6g (sat 2g)	**Cholesterol** 126mg
Protein 13g	**Sodium** 469mg
Carbohydrate 14g	

Exchanges: 1/2 starch, 1 vegetable, 1-1/2 lean meat, 1/2 fat

Creamy Oatmeal

Quick Recipe

3 cups fat-free milk
1-1/3 cups uncooked old-fashioned oats
1/2 cup raisins
4 teaspoons sugar substitute*
1/8 teaspoon salt

*This recipe was tested with SPLENDA® Granular.

1. Combine milk, oats, raisins, sugar substitute and salt in medium saucepan over medium heat.

2. Bring to a boil, stirring occasionally. Reduce heat and simmer 5 minutes. Cover; remove from heat. Let stand 5 minutes.   *Makes 6 servings*

Hint: For a quick, make-ahead breakfast, freeze oatmeal in individual portions. It can be reheated quickly in the microwave, saving the fuss of measuring, cooking and cleaning up.

Nutrients per Serving: 1 cup oatmeal

Calories 148	**Fiber** 2g
Fat 1g (sat <1g)	**Cholesterol** 1mg
Protein 7g	**Sodium** 116mg
Carbohydrate 29g	

Exchanges: 1/2 starch, 1 fruit, 1/2 milk

Strawberry Cheese Danish

Quick Recipe   (Pictured below right)

- 1/2 cup fat-free cream cheese, softened
- 2 tablespoons sugar substitute*
- 2 teaspoons lemon juice
- 1/2 teaspoon grated lemon peel
- 1 package (8 ounces) refrigerated reduced-fat crescent roll dough
- 8 teaspoons sugar-free strawberry preserves
- Powdered sugar (optional)

This recipe was tested with SPLENDA® Granular.

1. Preheat oven to 350°F. Combine cream cheese, sugar substitute, lemon juice and lemon peel in small bowl.

2. Separate dough into 4 rectangles; press perforations to seal. Work with one piece of dough at a time. Keep remaining dough on ungreased baking sheet in refrigerator.

3. Spread 2 tablespoons cream cheese mixture over top of 1 rectangle. Roll up lengthwise, pinching edge and ends to seal. Carefully stretch roll to about 12 inches. Cut in half. Shape halves into spirals on baking sheet in refrigerator, tucking ends under. Repeat with remaining dough rectangles and cream cheese mixture.

4. Make indentation in center of each roll; fill with 1 teaspoon preserves. Bake 14 to 16 minutes or until lightly browned. Remove to wire rack. Cool slightly. Sprinkle rolls with powdered sugar, if desired.   *Makes 8 servings*

Variation: Any flavor sugar-free preserves may be used in place of the strawberry preserves.

Nutrients per Serving: 1 danish

Calories 133	**Fiber** 1g
Fat 5g (sat 1g)	**Cholesterol** 3mg
Protein 4g	**Sodium** 334mg
Carbohydrate 20g	

Exchanges: 1-1/2 starch, 1 fat

Sunrise Pizza

Quick Recipe

- 2 small DOLE® Bananas, peeled
- 4 frozen waffles
- 1/4 cup low fat whipped cream cheese
- 1 can (11 ounces) DOLE® Mandarin Oranges, drained
- 2 teaspoons honey
- Dash ground cinnamon
- Fresh berries for garnish

• Thinly slice bananas on diagonal.

• Prepare waffles according to package directions.

• Spread waffle with cream cheese. Arrange banana slices on top, overlapping. Arrange orange segments in center of each pizza. Drizzle with honey. Sprinkle with cinnamon. Top with berries.   *Makes 4 servings*

Nutrients per Serving: 1 pizza (without berries)

Calories 205	**Fiber** 3g
Fat 5g (sat 2g)	**Cholesterol** 16mg
Protein 4g	**Sodium** 316mg
Carbohydrate 38g	

Exchanges: 1 starch, 1-1/2 fruit, 1 fat

Strawberry Cheese Danish

Glazed Coffee Cake Ring

low fat

(Pictured at right)

1/4 cup dried raisins or cranberries

1/2 cup water

1 package (11 ounces) refrigerated French bread dough

1 tablespoon sugar

1 tablespoon sugar substitute*

1 teaspoon ground cinnamon

1/4 teaspoon ground nutmeg

2 tablespoons reduced-sugar apricot fruit spread

1/3 cup sliced almonds or pecan chips, toasted**

*This recipe was tested with SPLENDA® Granular.

**To toast almonds, spread in single layer on baking sheet. Bake in preheated 350°F oven 8 to 10 minutes or until golden brown, stirring frequently.

1. Preheat oven to 350°F.

2. Place raisins in small microwavable bowl; cover with water. Microwave at HIGH 2 minutes.

3. Unroll dough on clean work surface. Combine sugar, sugar substitute, cinnamon and nutmeg in small bowl. Sprinkle mixture evenly over dough.

4. Drain raisins; sprinkle evenly over sugar-cinnamon mixture. Roll up dough, starting at wide end; pinch long seam to seal.

5. Spray nonstick baking sheet with nonstick cooking spray. Place dough roll, seam side down, on baking sheet. Join two ends to make a ring. Pinch ends tightly to seal. Using serrated knife, make 8 diagonal slits on top of dough. Bake 20 to 25 minutes or until golden. Remove to wire rack; let cool 5 minutes.

6. Place fruit spread in small microwavable bowl. Microwave at HIGH 15 seconds or until melted. Stir. Brush evenly over top and side of coffee cake. Sprinkle with almonds. Cut into 8 slices. Serve warm or at room temperature.

Makes 8 servings

Note: This recipe was tested in an 1100-watt microwave oven.

Nutrients per Serving: 1 slice coffee cake

Calories 146	**Fiber** 1g
Fat 3g (sat 1g)	**Cholesterol** 0mg
Protein 4g	**Sodium** 245mg
Carbohydrate 25g	

Exchanges: 1 starch, 1/2 fruit, 1/2 fat

৵ ৵ ৵

Orange Almond Honey Muffins

1-1/4 cups all-purpose flour

1 teaspoon baking powder

1/2 teaspoon baking soda

1/4 teaspoon salt

1/4 cup (1/2 stick) butter or margarine, softened

1/2 cup honey

1 egg

1/4 cup orange juice concentrate

1/2 teaspoon grated orange peel

1/2 cup chopped toasted almonds

In small bowl, combine flour, baking powder, baking soda and salt; set aside. Using an electric mixer, beat butter and honey until light. Beat in egg, orange juice concentrate and orange peel. Gradually add flour mixture, mixing until just blended; stir in almonds. Spoon into 8 greased or paper-lined 2-1/2-inch muffin cups. Bake at 350°F for 25 to 30 minutes, or until toothpick inserted into centers comes out clean. Remove muffins from pan to wire rack. Serve warm or at room temperature.

Makes 8 muffins

Favorite recipe from **National Honey Board**

Nutrients per Serving: 1 muffin

Calories 243	**Fiber** 1g
Fat 10g (sat 4g)	**Cholesterol** 41mg
Protein 4g	**Sodium** 214mg
Carbohydrate 37g	

Exchanges: 2-1/2 starch, 1-1/2 fat

Glazed Coffee Cake Ring

Main Dishes

ଓ ଓ ଓ

Basil Pork and Green Bean Stew

high fiber

Quick Recipe   *(Pictured at left)*

> 1 package (9 ounces) frozen cut green beans
> 3-1/2 cups peeled red potatoes, cut into 1/2-inch cubes
> 1 pound pork tenderloin, cut into 1-inch cubes
> 1 cup prepared no-sugar-added meatless spaghetti sauce
> 1/2 teaspoon salt
> 1 tablespoon chopped fresh basil *or* 1 teaspoon dried basil leaves
> 1/4 cup grated Parmesan cheese

Microwave Directions

1. Place beans in 4-quart microwavable casserole. Microwave, covered, at HIGH 3 minutes. Drain in colander.

2. Using same dish, microwave potatoes, covered, at HIGH 4 minutes. Stir in pork, beans, spaghetti sauce and salt. Microwave at HIGH 10 minutes, stirring halfway through cooking time. Stir in basil. Microwave 5 to 7 minutes or until potatoes are tender and meat is no longer pink in center. Serve with cheese.

Makes 6 servings

Note: This recipe was tested in an 1100-watt microwave oven.

Nutrients per Serving: 1 cup plus 2 tablespoons stew

Calories 274	**Fiber** 6g
Fat 4g (sat 2g)	**Cholesterol** 46mg
Protein 21g	**Sodium** 504mg
Carbohydrate 39g	

Exchanges: 2 starch, 1 vegetable, 2 lean meat

Clockwise from top left: Apple-Glazed Chicken Bundle (page 75), Basil Pork and Green Bean Stew, Chicken with Orange Almond Sauce (page 69) and Vegetarian Sausage Rice (page 66)

Turkey Vegetable Chili Mac

Quick Recipe   *(Pictured at right)*

- 3/4 pound 93% lean ground turkey breast
- 1/2 cup chopped onion
- 2 cloves garlic, minced
- 1 can (15 ounces) black beans, rinsed and drained
- 1 can (14-1/2 ounces) Mexican-style stewed tomatoes
- 1 can (14-1/2 ounces) diced tomatoes
- 1 cup frozen corn
- 1 teaspoon Mexican seasoning
- 1/2 cup uncooked elbow macaroni
- 6 tablespoons reduced-fat sour cream

1. Spray large nonstick saucepan or Dutch oven with nonstick cooking spray; heat over medium heat until hot. Add turkey, onion and garlic; cook 5 minutes or until turkey is no longer pink, stirring to separate turkey.

2. Stir beans, tomatoes, corn and Mexican seasoning into saucepan; bring to a boil over high heat. Cover; reduce heat to low. Simmer 15 minutes, stirring occasionally.

3. Meanwhile, cook pasta according to package directions, omitting salt. Rinse and drain pasta; stir into saucepan. Simmer, uncovered, 2 to 3 minutes or until heated through.

4. Top each serving with 1 tablespoon sour cream. *Makes 6 servings*

Nutrients per Serving: about 1 cup Chili Mac

Calories 218	**Fiber** 6g
Fat 2g (sat 1g)	**Cholesterol** 28mg
Protein 20g	**Sodium** 579mg
Carbohydrate 29g	

Exchanges: 1-1/2 starch, 1-1/2 vegetable, 2 lean meat

Vegetarian Sausage Rice

(Pictured on page 64)

- 2 cups chopped green bell peppers
- 1 can (15 ounces) dark kidney beans, rinsed and drained
- 1 can (14-1/2 ounces) diced tomatoes with green bell peppers and onions
- 1 cup chopped onion
- 1 cup sliced celery
- 1 cup water, divided
- 3/4 cup uncooked long-grain white rice
- 1-1/4 teaspoons salt
- 1 teaspoon hot pepper sauce (optional)
- 1/2 teaspoon dried thyme leaves
- 1/2 teaspoon dried red pepper flakes
- 3 bay leaves
- 1 package (8 ounces) frozen meatless breakfast patties, thawed
- 2 tablespoons olive oil
- 1/2 cup chopped fresh parsley

Slow Cooker Directions

1. Combine bell peppers, beans, tomatoes, onion, celery, 1/2 cup water, rice, salt, pepper sauce, if desired, thyme, red pepper flakes and bay leaves in slow cooker. Cover; cook on LOW 4 to 5 hours. Remove bay leaves; discard.

2. Dice breakfast patties. Heat oil in large nonstick skillet over medium-high heat. Add patties; cook 2 minutes or until lightly browned, scraping bottom of skillet occasionally. Transfer to slow cooker. Do not stir. Add remaining 1/2 cup water to skillet; bring to a boil over high heat 1 minute, scraping up bits on bottom of skillet. Add liquid and parsley to slow cooker; stir gently. Serve immediately. *Makes 8 servings*

Nutrients per Serving: 1 cup rice mixture

Calories 228	**Fiber** 8g
Fat 7g (sat 1g)	**Cholesterol** 0mg
Protein 11g	**Sodium** 891mg
Carbohydrate 33g	

Exchanges: 1-1/2 starch, 2 vegetable, 1 lean meat, 1/2 fat

Turkey Vegetable Chili Mac

Beef & Bean Burrito

Beef & Bean Burritos high fiber

Quick Recipe   *(Pictured above)*

- **1/2 pound boneless beef round steak, cut into 1/2-inch pieces**
- **3 cloves garlic, minced**
- **1 can (15 ounces) pinto beans, rinsed and drained**
- **1 can (4 ounces) diced mild green chilies, drained**
- **1/4 cup finely chopped fresh cilantro**
- **6 (7-inch) flour tortillas, warmed**
- **1/2 cup shredded reduced-fat Cheddar cheese**
- **Prepared salsa and fat-free sour cream (optional)**

1. Spray large nonstick skillet with nonstick cooking spray; heat over medium heat until hot. Add steak and garlic; cook and stir 5 minutes or until steak is cooked to desired doneness.

2. Add beans, chilies and cilantro; cook and stir 5 minutes or until heated through.

3. Divide steak mixture evenly among tortillas; sprinkle with cheese. Fold bottom end of tortilla over filling; roll to enclose. Repeat with remaining tortillas. Serve with salsa and sour cream, if desired.   *Makes 6 servings*

Nutrients per Serving: 1 burrito

Calories 304	**Fiber** 6g
Fat 8g (sat 2g)	**Cholesterol** 17mg
Protein 19g	**Sodium** 521mg
Carbohydrate 38g	

Exchanges: 2-1/2 starch, 1/2 vegetable, 1-1/2 lean meat, 1/2 fat

Chicken with Orange Almond Sauce

Quick Recipe (Pictured on page 64)

low sodium

Butter-flavored cooking spray
4 (4 ounces each) skinless boneless chicken breast halves
1 cup orange juice
1/3 cup SPLENDA® No Calorie Sweetener, Granular
2 tablespoons cornstarch
1 can (11 ounces) mandarin oranges, rinsed and drained
2 tablespoons slivered almonds
1 teaspoon dried onion flakes
1 teaspoon dried parsley flakes

1. In large skillet sprayed with cooking spray, brown chicken pieces for 4 to 5 minutes on each side.

2. Meanwhile, in covered jar, combine orange juice, SPLENDA® and cornstarch. Shake well to blend.

3. Pour sauce mixture into medium saucepan sprayed with cooking spray. Cook over medium heat until mixture thickens, stirring constantly. Remove from heat.

4. Stir mandarin oranges, almonds, onion flakes and parsley flakes into sauce. Spoon sauce evenly over browned chicken breasts.

5. Reduce heat and simmer for 5 minutes. When serving, evenly spoon sauce over chicken breasts. *Makes 4 servings*

Nutrients per Serving: 1/4 of total recipe

Calories 233	**Fiber** <1g
Fat 4g (sat 1g)	**Cholesterol** 66mg
Protein 28g	**Sodium** 85mg
Carbohydrate 21g	

Exchanges: 1/2 starch, 1 fruit, 3 lean meat

Veggie Tostadas

low fat **high fiber** **meatless**

1 tablespoon olive oil
1 cup chopped onion
1 cup chopped celery
2 large cloves garlic, chopped
1 can (15 ounces) red kidney beans, rinsed and drained
1 can (15 ounces) Great Northern beans, rinsed and drained
1 can (14-1/2 ounces) salsa-style diced tomatoes
2 teaspoons mild chili powder
1 teaspoon ground cumin
6 (6-inch) corn tortillas
Toppings: chopped fresh cilantro, shredded lettuce, chopped fresh tomatoes, shredded reduced-fat Cheddar cheese and fat-free sour cream (optional)

1. Heat oil in large skillet over medium heat. Add onion, celery and garlic. Cook and stir 8 minutes or until softened. Add beans and tomatoes. Stir to blend. Add chili powder and cumin; stir. Reduce heat to medium-low. Simmer 30 minutes, stirring occasionally, until thickened.

2. Meanwhile, preheat oven to 400°F. Place tortillas in single layer on baking sheet. Bake 10 to 12 minutes or until crisp. Place 1 tortilla on each plate. Spoon bean mixture evenly over each tortilla. Top with lettuce, tomatoes, Cheddar cheese and sour cream, if desired. *Makes 6 servings*

Nutrients per Serving: 1 tortilla with 2/3 cup bean mixture (without toppings)

Calories 208	**Fiber** 10g
Fat 3g (sat <1g)	**Cholesterol** 0mg
Protein 10g	**Sodium** 945mg
Carbohydrate 39g	

Exchanges: 2 starch, 1-1/2 vegetable, 1/2 fat

Gingered Chicken with Vegetables

Quick Recipe   *(Pictured at right)*

- 2 tablespoons vegetable oil, divided
- 1 pound boneless skinless chicken breasts, cut into thin strips
- 1 cup red pepper strips
- 1 cup sliced fresh mushrooms
- 16 fresh pea pods, cut in half crosswise
- 1/2 cup sliced water chestnuts
- 1/4 cup sliced green onions
- 1 tablespoon grated fresh gingerroot
- 1 large clove garlic, crushed
- 2/3 cup reduced-fat, reduced-sodium chicken broth
- 2 tablespoons EQUAL® SPOONFUL*
- 2 tablespoons light soy sauce
- 4 teaspoons cornstarch
- 2 teaspoons dark sesame oil
- Salt and pepper to taste

*May substitute 3 packets EQUAL® sweetener.

• Heat 1 tablespoon vegetable oil in large skillet over medium-high heat. Stir-fry chicken until no longer pink; remove chicken from skillet. Heat remaining 1 tablespoon vegetable oil in skillet. Add red peppers, mushrooms, pea pods, water chestnuts, green onions, ginger and garlic to skillet. Stir-fry mixture 3 to 4 minutes until vegetables are crisp-tender.

• Meanwhile, combine chicken broth, Equal®, soy sauce, cornstarch and sesame oil until smooth. Stir into skillet mixture. Cook over medium heat until thick and clear. Stir in chicken; heat through. Season with salt and pepper to taste.

• Serve over hot cooked rice, if desired.

Makes 4 servings

Nutrients per Serving: 1-1/2 cups (without added salt, pepper and rice)

Calories 263	**Fiber** 2g
Fat 11g (sat 1g)	**Cholesterol** 66mg
Protein 29g	**Sodium** 411mg
Carbohydrate 11g	

Exchanges: 2 vegetable, 3-1/2 lean meat, 1 fat

Saucy Broccoli and Spaghetti

Quick Recipe

- 3 ounces uncooked spaghetti
- 1 package (10 ounces) frozen chopped broccoli
- 1/2 cup thinly sliced leek, white part only
- 2 teaspoons cornstarch
- 1/2 cup fat-free milk
- 2 teaspoons chopped fresh oregano *or* 1/2 teaspoon dried oregano leaves
- 1/8 teaspoon hot pepper sauce
- 3 tablespoons reduced-fat cream cheese
- 1 tablespoon grated Romano or Parmesan cheese
- 1 tablespoon chopped fresh parsley

1. Prepare spaghetti according to package directions, omitting salt; drain and keep warm.

2. Meanwhile, cook broccoli and leek together according to package directions for broccoli, omitting salt. Drain, reserving 1/4 cup liquid. Add additional water, if needed, to make 1/4 cup. Set vegetables aside.

3. Combine cornstarch, milk, oregano and hot pepper sauce in medium saucepan. Stir in reserved 1/4 cup liquid. Cook and stir over medium heat until mixture boils and thickens. Stir in cream cheese. Cook and stir until cheese melts. Stir in vegetables; heat through.

4. Serve vegetable mixture with pasta. Sprinkle with Romano cheese and parsley.

Makes 4 servings

Nutrients per Serving: 3/4 cup pasta and vegetable mixture

Calories 162	**Fiber** 3g
Fat 3g (sat 2g)	**Cholesterol** 9mg
Protein 8g	**Sodium** 133mg
Carbohydrate 26g	

Exchanges: 1-1/2 starch, 1 vegetable, 1/2 fat

Gingered Chicken with Vegetables

Vegetable Lasagna

 meatless

(Pictured at right)

Tomato-Basil Sauce (recipe follows)
4 medium carrots, thinly sliced
3 medium zucchini, thinly sliced
6 ounces spinach, washed, stemmed and torn into bite-size pieces
1/4 teaspoon salt
1/4 teaspoon black pepper
2 egg whites
3 cups fat-free ricotta cheese
1/3 cup plus 2 tablespoons grated Parmesan cheese, divided
12 uncooked lasagna noodles
1-1/2 cups shredded part-skim mozzarella cheese
1-1/4 cups shredded reduced-fat Mexican cheese blend
1/2 cup water

1. Prepare Tomato-Basil Sauce.

2. Meanwhile, spray large nonstick skillet with nonstick cooking spray. Heat over medium heat until hot. Add carrots; cook and stir 4 minutes. Add zucchini; cook and stir 8 minutes or until crisp-tender. Add spinach; cook and stir 1 minute or until spinach is wilted. Stir in salt and pepper.

3. Preheat oven to 350°F. Whisk egg whites in medium bowl. Stir in ricotta cheese and 1/3 cup Parmesan cheese.

4. Spread 1 cup Tomato-Basil Sauce in bottom of 13×9-inch baking dish; top with 4 uncooked lasagna noodles. Spoon 1/3 of ricotta cheese mixture over noodles; carefully spread with spatula.

5. Spoon 1/3 of vegetable mixture over cheese. Top with 1 cup Tomato-Basil Sauce. Sprinkle with 1/2 cup *each* mozzarella and Mexican cheese blend. Repeat layers 2 times, beginning with noodles and ending with 1/4 cup Mexican cheese blend. Sprinkle with remaining 2 tablespoons Parmesan cheese.

6. Carefully pour water around sides of dish. Cover dish tightly with foil.

7. Bake lasagna 1 hour or until bubbly. Uncover. Let stand 10 to 15 minutes. Cut into 12 pieces to serve. *Makes 12 servings*

Tomato-Basil Sauce

2 cans (28 ounces each) plum tomatoes
1 medium onion, chopped
3 cloves garlic, minced
1 tablespoon sugar
1 tablespoon dried basil leaves
1/4 teaspoon salt
1/4 teaspoon black pepper

1. Drain tomatoes, reserving 1/2 cup juice. Seed and chop tomatoes.

2. Spray large nonstick skillet with nonstick cooking spray. Heat over medium heat until hot. Add onion and garlic; cook and stir 5 minutes or until tender.

3. Stir in tomatoes, reserved juice, sugar, basil, salt and pepper. Bring to a boil over high heat.

4. Reduce heat to low. Simmer, uncovered, 25 to 30 minutes or until most of juices have evaporated. *Makes 4 cups*

Nutrients per Serving: 1 piece lasagna

Calories 296	**Fiber** 4g
Fat 6g (sat 3g)	**Cholesterol** 30mg
Protein 20g	**Sodium** 664mg
Carbohydrate 39g	

Exchanges: 2 starch, 2 vegetable, 2 lean meat

Turkey Vegetable Crescent Pie

high fiber

2 cans (14 ounces each) fat-free reduced-sodium chicken broth

1 medium onion, diced

1-1/4 pounds boneless skinless turkey breast, cut into 3/4-inch pieces

3 cups diced unpeeled red potatoes

1 teaspoon chopped fresh rosemary *or* 1/2 teaspoon dried rosemary, crushed

1/4 teaspoon salt

1/8 teaspoon black pepper

1 package (16 ounces) frozen mixed vegetables

1 package (10 ounces) frozen mixed vegetables

3 tablespoons cornstarch

1/3 cup plus 1/2 cup fat-free milk

1 package (8 ounces) refrigerated reduced-fat crescent roll dough

1. Bring broth to a boil in large saucepan. Add onion; reduce heat and simmer 3 minutes. Add turkey to saucepan; return to a boil. Reduce heat; cover and simmer 7 to 9 minutes or until turkey is no longer pink. With slotted spoon, remove turkey from saucepan; place in 13×9-inch baking dish.

2. Return broth to a boil. Add potatoes, rosemary, salt and pepper; simmer 2 minutes. Return to a boil and stir in mixed vegetables. Simmer, covered, 7 to 8 minutes or until potatoes are tender. Remove vegetables with slotted spoon. Drain in colander set over bowl; reserve broth. Transfer vegetables to baking dish with turkey.

3. Preheat oven to 375°F.

4. Blend cornstarch with 1/3 cup milk in small bowl until smooth. Add enough remaining milk to reserved broth to equal 3 cups. Transfer to large saucepan. Bring to a boil over medium-high heat. Whisk in cornstarch mixture; return to a boil. Boil 1 minute or until thickened. Remove from heat; pour over turkey-vegetable mixture in baking dish.

5. Roll out crescent roll dough and seal at perforations. Roll out to 12×10-inch rectangle. Cut widthwise into 16 (10×3/4-inch) strips. For lattice top, arrange 8 strips diagonally over top, evenly spacing strips. Trim, if necessary. Arrange remaining strips diagonally in opposite direction over top. Trim, if necessary.

6. Bake 15 to 18 minutes or until crust is golden brown.   *Makes 8 servings*

Nutrients per Serving: 1 cup

Calories 309	**Fiber** 5g
Fat 5g (sat 1g)	**Cholesterol** 44mg
Protein 26g	**Sodium** 653mg
Carbohydrate 39g	

Exchanges: 2 starch, 2 vegetable, 2-1/2 lean meat

Tip

• Refrigerate perishable foods right after you get home from the store.

• Keep raw, cooked and ready-to-eat foods separate.

• Don't rinse or wash meat or poultry.

• Thaw foods properly.

Beef Bourguignonne

(Pictured at right)

- 1 to 2 boneless beef top sirloin steaks (about 3 pounds), trimmed of fat
- 1/2 cup all-purpose flour
- 4 slices bacon, diced
- 2 medium carrots, diced
- 8 small unpeeled red potatoes, cut into quarters
- 8 to 10 fresh mushrooms, sliced
- 20 to 24 pearl onions
- 3 cloves garlic, minced
- 1 bay leaf
- 1 teaspoon dried marjoram leaves
- 1/2 teaspoon dried thyme leaves
- 1/2 teaspoon salt
  - Black pepper
- 2-1/2 cups reduced-sodium beef broth

Slow Cooker Directions

1. Cut beef into 1-inch pieces. Coat with flour, shaking off excess; set aside.

2. Cook bacon in large skillet over medium heat until partially cooked. Add beef; brown on all sides. Drain fat.

3. Layer carrots, potatoes, mushrooms, onions, garlic, bay leaf, marjoram, thyme, salt, pepper to taste and beef mixture in slow cooker. Pour broth over all.

4. Cover; cook on LOW 8 to 9 hours or until beef is tender. Remove bay leaf; discard.

Makes 10 servings

Nutrients per Serving: about 1-1/3 cups Bourguignonne

Calories 268	**Fiber** 1g
Fat 7g (sat 3g)	**Cholesterol** 73mg
Protein 26g	**Sodium** 287mg
Carbohydrate 14g	

Exchanges: 1/2 starch, 1-1/2 vegetable, 3 lean meat, 1/2 fat

Light Tantalizing Tacos

Quick Recipe

- Cooking spray
- 1 medium onion, chopped
- 1 green bell pepper, chopped
- 3 cloves garlic, minced
- 1 package JENNIE-O TURKEY STORE® Extra Lean Ground Turkey Breast
- 1 tablespoon chili powder
- 1 teaspoon ground cumin
- 3/4 teaspoon salt (optional)
- 3/4 cup prepared salsa
- 12 (7-inch) soft flour tortillas
- 1-1/2 cups (6 ounces) shredded low-fat Cheddar cheese
- 1-1/2 cups shredded lettuce
- 1 cup chopped tomato
  - Optional toppings: fat-free or light sour cream, chopped cilantro, additional salsa

Coat large nonstick skillet with cooking spray and place over medium-high heat. Add onion, green pepper and garlic; cook 4 minutes, stirring occasionally. Crumble turkey into skillet; sprinkle with chili powder, cumin and salt. Cook 5 minutes or until turkey is no longer pink, stirring frequently. Add salsa; simmer 10 to 12 minutes or until sauce thickens. Spoon 1/3 cup mixture onto each tortilla; top with cheese, lettuce and tomato. Serve with desired toppings.

Makes 6 servings

Nutrients per Serving: 2 tacos (without added salt and toppings)

Calories 429	**Fiber** 4g
Fat 12g (sat 6g)	**Cholesterol** 58mg
Protein 35g	**Sodium** 700mg
Carbohydrate 43g	

Exchanges: 2-1/2 starch, 1 vegetable, 4 lean meat

Beef Bourguignonne

Turkey Vegetable Crescent Pie

high fiber

2 cans (14 ounces each) fat-free reduced-sodium chicken broth
1 medium onion, diced
1-1/4 pounds boneless skinless turkey breast, cut into 3/4-inch pieces
3 cups diced unpeeled red potatoes
1 teaspoon chopped fresh rosemary *or* 1/2 teaspoon dried rosemary, crushed
1/4 teaspoon salt
1/8 teaspoon black pepper
1 package (16 ounces) frozen mixed vegetables
1 package (10 ounces) frozen mixed vegetables
3 tablespoons cornstarch
1/3 cup plus 1/2 cup fat-free milk
1 package (8 ounces) refrigerated reduced-fat crescent roll dough

1. Bring broth to a boil in large saucepan. Add onion; reduce heat and simmer 3 minutes. Add turkey to saucepan; return to a boil. Reduce heat; cover and simmer 7 to 9 minutes or until turkey is no longer pink. With slotted spoon, remove turkey from saucepan; place in 13×9-inch baking dish.

2. Return broth to a boil. Add potatoes, rosemary, salt and pepper; simmer 2 minutes. Return to a boil and stir in mixed vegetables. Simmer, covered, 7 to 8 minutes or until potatoes are tender. Remove vegetables with slotted spoon. Drain in colander set over bowl; reserve broth. Transfer vegetables to baking dish with turkey.

3. Preheat oven to 375°F.

4. Blend cornstarch with 1/3 cup milk in small bowl until smooth. Add enough remaining milk to reserved broth to equal 3 cups. Transfer to large saucepan. Bring to a boil over medium-high heat. Whisk in cornstarch mixture; return to a boil. Boil 1 minute or until thickened. Remove from heat; pour over turkey-vegetable mixture in baking dish.

5. Roll out crescent roll dough and seal at perforations. Roll out to 12×10-inch rectangle. Cut widthwise into 16 (10×3/4-inch) strips. For lattice top, arrange 8 strips diagonally over top, evenly spacing strips. Trim, if necessary. Arrange remaining strips diagonally in opposite direction over top. Trim, if necessary.

6. Bake 15 to 18 minutes or until crust is golden brown. *Makes 8 servings*

Nutrients per Serving: 1 cup

Calories 309	Fiber 5g
Fat 5g (sat 1g)	Cholesterol 44mg
Protein 26g	Sodium 653mg
Carbohydrate 39g	

Exchanges: 2 starch, 2 vegetable, 2-1/2 lean meat

Tip

• Refrigerate perishable foods right after you get home from the store.

• Keep raw, cooked and ready-to-eat foods separate.

• Don't rinse or wash meat or poultry.

• Thaw foods properly.

Spaghetti Squash Primavera

Spaghetti Squash Primavera

 high fiber meatless cooking for 1 or 2

Quick Recipe   *(Pictured above)*

> 1 teaspoon olive oil
> 1/4 cup *each* diced green bell pepper, zucchini and carrot
> 1/4 cup *each* sliced mushrooms and green onions
> 2 cloves garlic, minced
> 1 plum tomato, diced
> 1 tablespoon red wine or water
> 1/2 teaspoon dried basil leaves
> 1/4 teaspoon salt
> 1/8 teaspoon black pepper
> 2 cups cooked spaghetti squash
> 2 tablespoons grated Parmesan cheese

Heat oil in medium skillet over low heat. Add bell pepper, zucchini, carrot, mushrooms, green onions and garlic; cook 10 to 12 minutes or until crisp-tender, stirring occasionally. Stir in tomato, wine or water, basil, salt and black pepper; cook 4 to 5 minutes, stirring once or twice. Serve vegetables over spaghetti squash. Top with cheese.   *Makes 2 servings*

Nutrients per Serving: 1 cup squash with 2/3 cup vegetables and 1 tablespoon cheese

Calories 116	**Fiber** 5g
Fat 5g (sat 1g)	**Cholesterol** 4mg
Protein 5g	**Sodium** 396mg
Carbohydrate 15g	

Exchanges: 3 vegetable, 1 fat

ఌ ఌ ఌ

Chunky Beef and Pepper Casserole with Noodles

Quick Recipe

> 1 pound 95% lean ground beef
> 1 cup chopped green bell pepper
> 1 cup chopped yellow onion
> 1 can (8 ounces) tomato sauce with basil, garlic and oregano
> 2 teaspoons Worcestershire sauce
> 4 ounces uncooked yolk-free egg noodles
> 1/4 teaspoon salt

1. Heat 12-inch nonstick skillet over medium-high heat until hot. Add beef; cook and stir 4 minutes or until no longer pink. Drain fat. Set beef aside.

2. Add pepper and onion to skillet; cook and stir 4 minutes or until onion is translucent. Return beef to skillet. Add tomato sauce and Worcestershire sauce; stir to blend. Bring to a boil. Reduce heat. Cover tightly; simmer 15 minutes or until onion is tender.

3. Meanwhile, cook noodles according to package directions, omitting salt. Remove meat mixture from heat; stir in salt. Cover; let stand 5 minutes. Serve beef mixture over cooked noodles.   *Makes 4 servings*

Nutrients per Serving: about 1 cup beef and pepper mixture with 1/2 cup cooked noodles

Calories 352	**Fiber** 4g
Fat 8g (sat 2g)	**Cholesterol** 66mg
Protein 31g	**Sodium** 432mg
Carbohydrate 36g	

Exchanges: 2 starch, 1 vegetable, 3 lean meat

Apple-Glazed Chicken Bundles

(Pictured on page 64)

> 1 tablespoon stick butter or margarine
> 1/4 cup thinly sliced green onions
> 2 cups dried unseasoned packaged bread cubes
> 1/3 cup dried cranberries
> 1/3 cup apple juice
> 1/3 cup water
> 2 tablespoons EQUAL® SPOONFUL™*
> 1/4 teaspoon salt
> 1/8 teaspoon freshly ground black pepper
> 4 boneless skinless chicken breast halves (6 ounces each), pounded to 1/4-inch thickness
> 1-1/2 cups apple juice
> 1/2 cup water
> 2 tablespoons cornstarch
> 1 tablespoon lemon juice
> 2 tablespoons EQUAL® SPOONFUL™*
> Salt and pepper to taste

*May substitute 3 packets EQUAL® sweetener.

1. Preheat oven to 350°F. Melt butter in small skillet. Add green onions; cook 1 to 2 minutes until tender. Place bread cubes and dried cranberries in medium bowl. Add onion mixture. Combine and heat 1/3 cup apple juice and 1/3 cup water almost to a boil. Stir into bread cube mixture until all cubes are moistened. Stir in 2 tablespoons Equal®, salt and pepper; mix well.

2. Lay chicken breasts on flat surface. Sprinkle with salt and pepper, if desired. Place 1/2 cup stuffing mixture in center of each chicken breast. Fold in sides of chicken to form "bundle." Secure each with wooden picks. Place in shallow baking pan sprayed with nonstick cooking spray. Bake in preheated 350°F oven 35 to 40 minutes or until chicken and stuffing reach 160°F and chicken juices are clear when chicken is pierced with fork.

3. Meanwhile, combine 1-1/2 cups apple juice, 1/2 cup water, cornstarch and lemon juice in small saucepan; stir until smooth. Bring to a boil over medium heat, stirring frequently. Boil and stir until thickened. Remove from heat; stir in 2 tablespoons Equal®. Spoon over chicken. Add salt and pepper to taste. *Makes 4 servings*

Nutrients per Serving: 1 bundle (without additional salt and pepper seasoning)

Calories 370	Fiber 1g
Fat 6g (sat 2g)	Cholesterol 107mg
Protein 41g	Sodium 379mg
Carbohydrate 36g	

Exchanges: 1 starch, 1 fruit, 5 lean meat

ᔕ ᔕ ᔕ

Cajun Chicken Drums

> 4 chicken drumsticks, skin removed
> 1/2 to 3/4 teaspoon Cajun seasoning
> 1/2 teaspoon grated lemon peel
> 2 tablespoons lemon juice
> 1/2 teaspoon hot pepper sauce (optional)
> 1/8 teaspoon salt
> 2 tablespoons finely chopped fresh parsley

1. Preheat oven to 400°F. Spray shallow baking dish with nonstick cooking spray. Add chicken to dish and sprinkle evenly with Cajun seasoning. Cover dish with foil and bake 25 minutes, turning drumsticks once.

2. Remove foil and bake 15 to 20 minutes more or until drumsticks are cooked through. Remove from oven. Add remaining ingredients to dish; toss to coat, scraping bottom and sides of dish with spatula. *Makes 2 servings*

Nutrients per Serving: 2 drumsticks

Calories 173	Fiber <1g
Fat 5g (sat 1g)	Cholesterol 108mg
Protein 29g	Sodium 254mg
Carbohydrate 2g	

Exchanges: 3-1/2 lean meat

Beef Bourguignonne

(Pictured at right)

1 to 2 boneless beef top sirloin steaks (about 3 pounds), trimmed of fat
1/2 cup all-purpose flour
4 slices bacon, diced
2 medium carrots, diced
8 small unpeeled red potatoes, cut into quarters
8 to 10 fresh mushrooms, sliced
20 to 24 pearl onions
3 cloves garlic, minced
1 bay leaf
1 teaspoon dried marjoram leaves
1/2 teaspoon dried thyme leaves
1/2 teaspoon salt
Black pepper
2-1/2 cups reduced-sodium beef broth

Slow Cooker Directions

1. Cut beef into 1-inch pieces. Coat with flour, shaking off excess; set aside.

2. Cook bacon in large skillet over medium heat until partially cooked. Add beef; brown on all sides. Drain fat.

3. Layer carrots, potatoes, mushrooms, onions, garlic, bay leaf, marjoram, thyme, salt, pepper to taste and beef mixture in slow cooker. Pour broth over all.

4. Cover; cook on LOW 8 to 9 hours or until beef is tender. Remove bay leaf; discard.

Makes 10 servings

Nutrients per Serving: about 1-1/3 cups Bourguignonne

Calories 268	**Fiber** 1g
Fat 7g (sat 3g)	**Cholesterol** 73mg
Protein 26g	**Sodium** 287mg
Carbohydrate 14g	

Exchanges: 1/2 starch, 1-1/2 vegetable, 3 lean meat, 1/2 fat

Light Tantalizing Tacos

Quick Recipe

Cooking spray
1 medium onion, chopped
1 green bell pepper, chopped
3 cloves garlic, minced
1 package JENNIE-O TURKEY STORE® Extra Lean Ground Turkey Breast
1 tablespoon chili powder
1 teaspoon ground cumin
3/4 teaspoon salt (optional)
3/4 cup prepared salsa
12 (7-inch) soft flour tortillas
1-1/2 cups (6 ounces) shredded low-fat Cheddar cheese
1-1/2 cups shredded lettuce
1 cup chopped tomato
Optional toppings: fat-free or light sour cream, chopped cilantro, additional salsa

Coat large nonstick skillet with cooking spray and place over medium-high heat. Add onion, green pepper and garlic; cook 4 minutes, stirring occasionally. Crumble turkey into skillet; sprinkle with chili powder, cumin and salt. Cook 5 minutes or until turkey is no longer pink, stirring frequently. Add salsa; simmer 10 to 12 minutes or until sauce thickens. Spoon 1/3 cup mixture onto each tortilla; top with cheese, lettuce and tomato. Serve with desired toppings. *Makes 6 servings*

Nutrients per Serving: 2 tacos (without added salt and toppings)

Calories 429	**Fiber** 4g
Fat 12g (sat 6g)	**Cholesterol** 58mg
Protein 35g	**Sodium** 700mg
Carbohydrate 43g	

Exchanges: 2-1/2 starch, 1 vegetable, 4 lean meat

Sausage and Cheese Pizza

Quick Recipe   *(Pictured at right)*

> 1 package (about 13 ounces) refrigerated pizza crust dough
> 1 medium red onion, thinly sliced
> 1/4 pound cooked turkey sausage breakfast links (5 to 6 links), thinly sliced
> 1 medium green bell pepper, thinly sliced
> 3/4 cup pizza sauce
> Dried red pepper flakes (optional)
> 1 cup shredded reduced-fat Mexican cheese blend or pizza cheese blend

1. Preheat oven to 425°F. Spray 15×10-inch jelly-roll pan with nonstick cooking spray. Unroll dough on pan; press to edges of pan. Bake about 6 minutes or until crust begins to brown.

2. Meanwhile, spray large nonstick skillet with nonstick cooking spray. Heat over medium-high heat. Add onion; cook and stir until tender.

3. Add sausage and bell pepper to skillet. Cook and stir about 5 minutes or until bell pepper is crisp-tender.

4. Spread pizza sauce evenly over crust to within 1/2 inch of edge; top with sausage mixture. Sprinkle with red pepper flakes, if desired. Top with cheese. Bake 7 to 10 minutes or until pizza is golden brown and cheese is melted. Cut pizza into 8 pieces to serve.   *Makes 8 servings*

Nutrients per Serving: 1 piece pizza

Calories 212	**Fiber** 1g
Fat 7g (sat 3g)	**Cholesterol** 19mg
Protein 11g	**Sodium** 618mg
Carbohydrate 26g	

Exchanges: 1-1/2 starch, 1/2 vegetable, 1 lean meat, 1/2 fat

Rosemary-Lemon Pork Kabobs

Quick Recipe

> 4 small new potatoes, quartered
> 1 pound pork tenderloin, trimmed of fat and cut into 16 (1-inch) cubes
> 1 small onion (2 ounces) quartered and layers separated
> Nonstick cooking spray
> 1/2 teaspoon dried rosemary, crushed
> Dash paprika
> 2 tablespoons lemon juice
> 1 tablespoon olive oil
> 1 teaspoon grated lemon peel
> 1/2 medium clove garlic, minced
> 1/2 teaspoon salt
> 1/8 teaspoon black pepper

1. Preheat broiler.

2. Steam potatoes 6 minutes or until just crisp-tender. Rinse under cold water to cool. Dry with paper towels.

3. Place potatoes on 4 (10-inch) metal skewers, alternating with pork and onion. Spray lightly with cooking spray; sprinkle with rosemary and paprika.

4. Place kabobs on baking sheet; broil 4 minutes. Turn over; broil 4 minutes more or until pork is barely pink in center.

5. Meanwhile, combine remaining ingredients in small bowl; set aside.

6. To serve, brush lemon mixture evenly over kabobs.   *Makes 4 servings*

Nutrients per Serving: 1 kabob

Calories 212	**Fiber** 1g
Fat 7g (sat 2g)	**Cholesterol** 73mg
Protein 25g	**Sodium** 338mg
Carbohydrate 11g	

Exchanges: 1 starch, 3 lean meat

Thai Curry Stir-Fry

Quick Recipe   *(Pictured at right)*

>   2 teaspoons cornstarch
> 1/2 cup fat-free reduced-sodium chicken
>   broth
>   2 teaspoons reduced-sodium soy sauce
> 1-1/2 teaspoons curry powder
> 1/8 teaspoon dried red pepper flakes
>   Nonstick olive oil cooking spray
>   3 green onions, sliced
>   2 cloves garlic, minced
>   2 cups fresh broccoli florets
> 2/3 cup sliced carrot
> 1-1/2 teaspoons olive oil
>   6 ounces boneless skinless chicken
>   breasts, cut into bite-size pieces
> 2/3 cup hot cooked rice

1. Stir together cornstarch, broth, soy sauce, curry powder and red pepper flakes in small bowl. Set aside.

2. Spray nonstick wok or large nonstick skillet with cooking spray. Heat over medium-high heat. Add onions and garlic; stir-fry 1 minute. Remove from wok.

3. Add broccoli and carrot to wok; stir-fry 2 to 3 minutes or until crisp-tender. Remove from wok.

4. Add oil to hot wok. Add chicken and stir-fry 2 to 3 minutes or until no longer pink. Stir broth mixture. Add to wok. Cook and stir until broth mixture comes to a boil and thickens slightly. Return all vegetables to wok. Heat through.

5. Serve with rice.   *Makes 2 servings*

Nutrients per Serving: 1/2 of total recipe

Calories 273	**Fiber** 5g
Fat 6g (sat 1g)	**Cholesterol** 57mg
Protein 28g	**Sodium** 308mg
Carbohydrate 27g	

Exchanges: 1 starch, 2-1/2 vegetable, 3 lean meat

Impossibly Easy Salmon Pie

>   1 can (7-1/2 ounces) salmon packed in
>   water, drained and deboned
> 1/2 cup grated Parmesan cheese
> 1/4 cup sliced green onions
>   1 jar (2 ounces) chopped pimientos,
>   drained
> 1/2 cup 1% cottage cheese
>   1 tablespoon lemon juice
> 1-1/2 cups 1% milk
> 3/4 cup reduced-fat baking and pancake mix
>   2 eggs
>   2 egg whites *or* 1/4 cup egg substitute
> 1/4 teaspoon dried dill weed
> 1/4 teaspoon paprika (optional)

1. Preheat oven to 375°F. Spray 9-inch pie plate with nonstick cooking spray.

2. Combine salmon, Parmesan cheese, onions and pimientos in prepared pie plate; set aside.

3. Combine cottage cheese and lemon juice in blender or food processor. Cover and blend until smooth. Add milk, baking mix, whole eggs, egg whites and dill. Blend 15 seconds. Pour over salmon mixture in pie plate. Sprinkle with paprika, if desired.

4. Bake 35 to 40 minutes or until lightly golden and knife inserted halfway between center and edge comes out clean. Cool 5 minutes. Cut into 6 wedges to serve.   *Makes 6 servings*

Nutrients per Serving: 1 pie wedge

Calories 204	**Fiber** <1g
Fat 8g (sat 3g)	**Cholesterol** 100mg
Protein 19g	**Sodium** 633mg
Carbohydrate 15g	

Exchanges: 1 starch, 2-1/2 lean meat

Thai Curry Stir-Fry

Blackened Catfish with Easy Tartar Sauce and Rice

Blackened Catfish with Easy Tartar Sauce and Rice

Quick Recipe (Pictured above)

Easy Tartar Sauce (recipe follows)
4 catfish fillets (about 1/4 pound each)
2 teaspoons fresh lemon juice
   Nonstick garlic-flavored cooking spray
2 teaspoons blackened or Cajun
   seasoning blend
2 cups hot cooked rice

1. Prepare Easy Tartar Sauce.

2. Rinse catfish and pat dry with paper towels. Sprinkle with lemon juice; coat with cooking spray. Sprinkle with seasoning blend; coat again with cooking spray.

3. Heat large nonstick skillet over medium-high heat until hot. Add 2 fillets to skillet, seasoned side down. Cook 3 minutes per side. Reduce heat to medium and cook 3 minutes more or until fish begins to flake when tested with a fork. Remove fillets from skillet; keep warm. Repeat with remaining fillets. Serve with tartar sauce and rice.   *Makes 4 servings*

Easy Tartar Sauce

1/4 cup fat-free or reduced-fat mayonnaise
2 tablespoons sweet pickle relish
1 teaspoon fresh lemon juice

Combine mayonnaise, relish and lemon juice in small bowl; mix well. Refrigerate until ready to serve.   *Makes about 1/4 cup*

Nutrients per Serving: 1 fillet with 1 tablespoon tartar sauce and 1/2 cup cooked rice

Calories 290	**Fiber** 1g
Fat 8g (sat 2g)	**Cholesterol** 54mg
Protein 19g	**Sodium** 344mg
Carbohydrate 33g	

Exchanges: 2 starch, 2 lean meat, 1 fat

Tip

Store tightly wrapped fresh fish in the refrigerator for a day or two at the most. Double-wrapped frozen fish can be stored in the freezer for up to 6 months. It takes about 24 hours to thaw 1 pound of frozen fish in the refrigerator. Or, that same pound can be quick-thawed, still wrapped, in cold water in about an hour.

Stuffed Bell Pepper

Stuffed Bell Peppers

 high fiber meatless

(Pictured above)

1 package (8-1/2 ounces) cornbread mix
   plus ingredients to prepare
6 medium green bell peppers
1 large onion, thinly sliced
1 teaspoon olive oil
1 can (14-1/2 ounces) diced tomatoes
1 package (10 ounces) frozen corn,
   thawed and drained
1 can (2-1/4 ounces) sliced ripe olives,
   drained
1/3 cup raisins
1 tablespoon chili powder
1 teaspoon ground sage
1 cup shredded reduced-fat Mexican
   cheese blend, divided

1. Prepare cornbread according to package directions. Cut into cubes. *Reduce oven temperature to 350°F.*

2. Slice tops off bell peppers; discard stems and seeds. Finely chop tops to equal 1 cup; set aside. Rinse peppers. Bring 2 to 3 inches water to a boil over high heat in large saucepan. Add 1 or more peppers and boil 1 minute, turning peppers with tongs to blanch evenly. Rinse with cold water; drain. Repeat with remaining peppers.

3. Place onion and oil in Dutch oven. Cover and cook over medium-high heat, stirring occasionally, 8 to 10 minutes or until onion is tender and browned. Add 1 to 2 tablespoons water, if needed, to prevent sticking. Add chopped bell pepper; cook and stir 1 minute more. Remove from heat.

4. Add tomatoes, corn, olives, raisins, chili powder and sage to Dutch oven; stir. Stir in corn bread (it will crumble) and 3/4 cup cheese. Spoon filling into peppers. Top with remaining 1/4 cup cheese. Place peppers in baking dish; bake 20 to 30 minutes or until heated through.

Makes 6 servings

Nutrients per Serving: 1 stuffed pepper

Calories 374	Fiber 8g
Fat 12g (sat 4g)	Cholesterol 46mg
Protein 13g	Sodium 854mg
Carbohydrate 57g	

Exchanges: 3 starch, 2-1/2 vegetable, 1 lean meat, 1 fat

Tip

Two egg whites and 1/3 cup fat-free milk were used to prepare the cornbread mix for this recipe, instead of the full-fat ingredients called for in the package directions.

Grilled Salmon Fillet, Asparagus and Onions

Grilled Salmon Fillets, Asparagus and Onions

(Pictured above)

1/2 teaspoon paprika
6 salmon fillets (6 ounces each)
1/3 cup bottled fat-free honey-Dijon
    dressing or barbecue sauce
1 bunch (about 1 pound) fresh asparagus
    spears, ends trimmed
1 large red or sweet onion, cut into
    1/4-inch-thick slices
1 tablespoon olive oil
    Salt and black pepper (optional)

1. Spray cold grid of grill with nonstick cooking spray. Prepare grill for direct grilling. Sprinkle paprika over salmon fillets. Brush marinade over salmon; let stand at room temperature 15 minutes.

2. Brush asparagus and onion slices with olive oil; season to taste with salt and pepper, if desired.

3. Place salmon, skin side down, in center of grid over medium coals. Arrange asparagus spears and onion slices around salmon. Grill salmon and vegetables on covered grill 5 minutes. Turn salmon, asparagus and onion slices. Grill 5 to 6 minutes more or until salmon flakes when tested with a fork and vegetables are crisp-tender. Separate onion slices into rings; arrange over asparagus. *Makes 6 servings*

Nutrients per Serving: 1 salmon fillet with 3/4 cup asparagus and onion mixture

Calories 399	**Fiber** 1g
Fat 22g (sat 4g)	**Cholesterol** 100mg
Protein 37g	**Sodium** 439mg
Carbohydrate 11g	

Exchanges: 2 vegetable, 5 lean meat, 1-1/2 fat

Tip

You'll notice this recipe is particularly high in fat. Salmon, however, is high in a good kind of fat—omega-3 fatty acids. These fats are believed to lower your risk for heart disease and play a role in healthy immune function. You can feel good about indulging in this scrumptious dish. Simply plan other lower-fat foods around it.

Double Spinach Bake

meatless

8 ounces uncooked spinach fettuccine noodles

1 cup sliced fresh mushrooms

1 green onion, finely chopped

1 clove garlic, minced

4-1/2 cups fresh spinach, washed, stemmed and coarsely chopped *or* 1 package (10 ounces) frozen spinach, thawed and drained

1 tablespoon water

1 container (15 ounces) fat-free ricotta cheese

1/4 cup fat-free milk

1 egg

1/2 teaspoon ground nutmeg

1/2 teaspoon black pepper

1/4 cup shredded reduced-fat Swiss cheese

1. Preheat oven to 350°F. Cook noodles according to package directions, omitting salt. Drain; set aside.

2. Spray medium nonstick skillet with nonstick cooking spray. Add mushrooms, green onion and garlic. Cook and stir over medium heat until mushrooms are softened. Add spinach and water. Cover; cook about 3 minutes or until spinach is wilted.

3. Combine ricotta cheese, milk, egg, nutmeg and pepper in large bowl. Gently stir in noodles and vegetables; toss to coat evenly.

4. Lightly spray shallow 1-1/2-quart baking dish with cooking spray. Spread noodle mixture in dish. Sprinkle with Swiss cheese.

5. Bake 25 to 30 minutes or until knife inserted halfway into center comes out clean.

Makes 6 servings

Nutrients per Serving: 1 cup casserole

Calories 214	**Fiber** 3g
Fat 4g (sat 1g)	**Cholesterol** 90mg
Protein 19g	**Sodium** 244mg
Carbohydrate 25g	

Exchanges: 1-1/2 starch, 1 vegetable, 2 lean meat

Cheese Tortellini with Tuna

1 tuna steak* (about 6 ounces)

1 package (9 ounces) uncooked refrigerated cheese tortellini

1 cup finely chopped red bell pepper

1 cup finely chopped green bell pepper

1/4 cup finely chopped onion

3/4 teaspoon fennel seeds, crushed

1/2 cup evaporated fat-free milk

2 teaspoons all-purpose flour

1/2 teaspoon dry mustard

1/2 teaspoon black pepper

*Or, substitute 1 can (6 ounces) tuna packed in water, drained, for tuna steak. Omit step 1.

1. Grill or broil tuna 4 inches from heat source about 7 to 9 minutes or until fish just begins to flake, turning once. Remove and discard skin. Cut tuna into chunks; set aside.

2. Cook pasta according to package directions, omitting salt. Drain; set aside.

3. Spray large nonstick skillet with nonstick cooking spray. Add bell peppers, onion and fennel seeds; cook, stirring occasionally, over medium heat until crisp-tender.

4. Whisk together milk, flour, mustard and black pepper in small bowl until smooth; add to skillet. Cook until thickened, stirring constantly. Stir in tuna and pasta; reduce heat to low and simmer about 3 minutes or until heated through. Serve immediately. *Makes 4 servings*

Nutrients per Serving: 1-1/4 cups

Calories 250	**Fiber** 2g
Fat 4g (sat 1g)	**Cholesterol** 38mg
Protein 21g	**Sodium** 230mg
Carbohydrate 32g	

Exchanges: 2 starch, 1/2 vegetable, 2 lean meat

Pork and Plum Kabobs

Quick Recipe   *(Pictured at right)*

> **3/4 pound boneless pork loin chops (1 inch thick), trimmed of fat and cut into 1-inch pieces**
> **1-1/2 teaspoons ground cumin**
> **1/2 teaspoon ground cinnamon**
> **1/4 teaspoon salt**
> **1/4 teaspoon garlic powder**
> **1/4 teaspoon ground red pepper**
> **1/4 cup sliced green onions**
> **1/4 cup reduced-sugar red raspberry fruit spread**
> **1 tablespoon orange juice**
> **3 medium plums, seeded and cut into wedges**

1. Place pork in large resealable plastic bag. Combine cumin, cinnamon, salt, garlic powder and red pepper in small bowl. Sprinkle over meat in bag. Shake to coat meat with spices.

2. Spray cold grid of grill with nonstick cooking spray. Prepare grill for direct grilling. Combine green onions, raspberry spread and orange juice in small bowl; set aside.

3. Alternately thread plum and pork wedges onto 8 metal or soaked wooden skewers. Grill kabobs, covered, directly over medium heat 12 to 14 minutes or until meat is barely pink in center, turning once during grilling. Brush frequently with reserved raspberry mixture during last 5 minutes of grilling.   *Makes 4 servings*

Serving Suggestion: A crisp, cool salad makes a great side to these sweet grilled kabobs.

Nutrients per Serving: 2 kabobs

Calories 191	**Fiber** 1g
Fat 5g (sat 2g)	**Cholesterol** 53mg
Protein 19g	**Sodium** 183mg
Carbohydrate 17g	

Exchanges: 1 fruit, 2-1/2 lean meat

Sirloin with Sweet Caramelized Onions

Quick Recipe

> **1 medium onion, very thinly sliced**
> **1 boneless beef top sirloin steak (about 1 pound), trimmed of fat**
> **1/4 cup water**
> **2 tablespoons Worcestershire sauce**
> **1 tablespoon sugar**

1. Lightly spray 12-inch nonstick skillet with nonstick cooking spray; heat over high heat until hot. Add onion; cook and stir 4 minutes or until browned. Remove from skillet and set aside. Wipe out skillet with paper towel.

2. Spray same skillet with cooking spray; heat over medium-high heat until hot. Add beef; cook 10 to 13 minutes for medium-rare to medium, turning once. Remove from heat and transfer to cutting board; let stand 3 minutes.

3. Meanwhile, return skillet to high heat until hot; add onion, water, Worcestershire sauce and sugar. Cook 30 to 45 seconds or until most liquid has evaporated.

4. Thinly slice beef on the diagonal and serve with onions.   *Makes 4 servings*

Nutrients per Serving: 1/4 of beef (about 3 ounces cooked weight) with 2-1/2 tablespoons onions

Calories 159	**Fiber** 1g
Fat 5g (sat 2g)	**Cholesterol** 60mg
Protein 21g	**Sodium** 118mg
Carbohydrate 7g	

Exchanges: 1/2 starch, 3 lean meat

Ham with Peach Sauce

Quick Recipe   *(Pictured at right)*

1 boneless extra-lean ham steak (about 1 pound)
1 clove garlic, minced
1/2 cup fat-free reduced-sodium chicken broth
2 large peaches, peeled and sliced *or* 2 cups frozen unsweetened sliced peaches, thawed
1-1/2 teaspoon lemon juice
2 tablespoons thinly sliced green onions

1. Heat large nonstick skillet over medium-high heat until hot. Place ham in skillet; cook, turning once, about 4 minutes or until well browned on both sides. Remove ham from skillet. Cover loosely with foil to keep warm.

2. Add garlic to skillet; cook and stir 30 seconds. Stir in broth. Increase heat to high. Bring to a boil; cook 5 minutes or until slightly thickened. Stir in peaches; cook about 2 minutes or until softened. Stir in lemon juice. Transfer mixture to blender or food processor; cover and blend until coarsely puréed.

3. Cut ham into 4 pieces. Spoon peach sauce over ham. Sprinkle with green onions.

Makes 4 servings

Nutrients per Serving: 1 piece ham (1/4 of ham steak) with 1/2 cup peach sauce

Calories 169	**Fiber** 1g
Fat 5g (sat 2g)	**Cholesterol** 51mg
Protein 24g	**Sodium** 1488mg
Carbohydrate 8g	

Exchanges: 1/2 fruit, 2-1/2 lean meat

Shrimp & Snow Peas with Rotini

Quick Recipe

6 ounces (about 2 cups) uncooked rotini
2 cloves garlic, finely chopped
1/4 teaspoon dried red pepper flakes
3/4 pound uncooked medium shrimp, peeled and deveined
2 cups fresh snow peas
2 tablespoons water
1 can (8 ounces) sliced water chestnuts, drained
1/3 cup sliced green onions
3 tablespoons lime juice
2 tablespoons chopped fresh cilantro
2 tablespoons olive oil
1 tablespoon reduced-sodium soy sauce
1-1/2 teaspoons Mexican seasoning

1. Cook pasta according to package directions, omitting salt; drain. Set aside.

2. Spray large nonstick skillet with nonstick cooking spray; heat over medium heat until hot. Add garlic and red pepper; stir-fry 1 minute. Add shrimp; stir-fry 5 minutes or until shrimp are opaque. Remove shrimp from skillet.

3. Add snow peas and water to skillet; cook, covered, 1 minute. Uncover; cook and stir 2 minutes or until snow peas are crisp-tender. Remove snow peas from skillet.

4. Combine pasta, shrimp, snow peas, water chestnuts and onions in large bowl. Blend lime juice, cilantro, oil, soy sauce and Mexican seasoning in small bowl. Drizzle over pasta mixture; toss to coat.

Makes 6 servings

Nutrients per Serving: 1 cup plus 3 tablespoons

Calories 169	**Fiber** 3g
Fat 5g (sat 1g)	**Cholesterol** 87mg
Protein 13g	**Sodium** 244mg
Carbohydrate 18g	

Exchanges: 1 starch, 1/2 vegetable, 1-1/2 lean meat

Ham with Peach Sauce

Crispy Baked Chicken

Crispy Baked Chicken

low fat

(Pictured above)

1 cup (8 ounces) fat-free French onion dip
1/2 cup fat-free milk
1 cup cornflake crumbs
1/2 cup wheat germ
6 skinless chicken breast halves or thighs (about 1/4 pound each)

1. Preheat oven to 350°F. Spray shallow baking dish with nonstick cooking spray.

2. Place dip in shallow bowl; stir until smooth. Add milk, 1 tablespoon at a time, until pourable consistency is reached.

3. Combine cornflake crumbs and wheat germ on plate.

4. Dip chicken pieces in milk mixture, then roll in cornflake mixture. Place chicken in single layer in prepared dish. Bake 45 to 50 minutes or until juices run clear when chicken is pierced with fork and chicken is no longer pink near bone. *Makes 6 servings*

Nutrients per Serving: 1 breast

Calories 212	**Fiber** 1g
Fat 1g (sat <1g)	**Cholesterol** 59mg
Protein 27g	**Sodium** 484mg
Carbohydrate 22g	

Exchanges: 1-1/2 starch, 3 lean meat

Vegetable-Enchilada Casserole

 high fiber · meatless

1 small eggplant, peeled and quartered
1 medium zucchini
1/2 pound fresh mushrooms
    Nonstick cooking spray
1/2 cup chopped green onions, divided
2 cloves garlic, minced
1 jar (16 ounces) GUILTLESS GOURMET®
    Southwestern Grill Salsa
1 (7-ounce) bag GUILTLESS GOURMET®
    Baked Tortilla chips (yellow, red or
    blue corn)
1 jar (16 ounces) GUILTLESS GOURMET®
    Black Bean Dip (Spicy or Mild)
3/4 cup low fat shredded Cheddar cheese
2-1/2 cups shredded lettuce
1 medium tomato, chopped
3 tablespoons low fat sour cream

Slice eggplant, zucchini and mushrooms; set aside. Coat large nonstick skillet with cooking spray. Heat over medium-high heat until hot. Add reserved vegetables, 1/4 cup onions and garlic; cover and cook 5 minutes or until tender, stirring occasionally. Stir in salsa. Reduce heat to low; cover and simmer 30 minutes. Preheat oven to 350°F. To assemble casserole, coat 12×8-inch baking dish with cooking spray. Arrange half the tortilla chips in dish and top with vegetable mixture. Cover; bake 20 to 30 minutes or until heated through. Dollop with rounded teaspoons of black bean dip on top of vegetables. Coarsely crush remaining tortilla chips; sprinkle over vegetable mixture. Sprinkle cheese over chips. Bake, uncovered, 5 minutes or more until chips are crisp and lightly browned. To serve, divided lettuce among 8 individual serving plates or spread on serving platter. Spoon casserole over lettuce. Sprinkle with chopped tomato and remaining 1/4 cup onions. Dollop with sour cream.   *Makes 8 servings*

Nutrients per Serving: about 1-1/4 cups

Calories 242	**Fiber** 7g
Fat 4g (sat 1g)	**Cholesterol** 6mg
Protein 12g	**Sodium** 699mg
Carbohydrate 41g	

Exchanges: 2 starch, 2 vegetable, 1/2 lean meat, 1/2 fat

Pork Chops with Red Cabbage and Apples

low sodium · high fiber

1 teaspoon Chinese 5-spice powder*
1/2 teaspoon salt substitute
1/2 teaspoon black pepper
3 center-cut pork loin chops (about
    1/4 pound each), trimmed of fat
2 teaspoons olive oil
1 large Granny Smith apple, cored and
    sliced
2 tablespoons chopped shallots
1 teaspoon butter
1/2 head red cabbage, grated (about 4 cups)
1 teaspoon sugar substitute**
1/2 teaspoon red wine vinegar
1/2 teaspoon lemon juice
6 tablespoons unsweetened applesauce
    (optional)

Chinese 5-spice powder is a blend of cinnamon, cloves, fennel seed, anise and Szechuan peppercorns.

**This recipe was tested with SPLENDA® Granular.*

1. Mix 5-spice powder, salt substitute and pepper in small bowl. Sprinkle mixture evenly over pork chops; set aside. Heat oil 1 minute in large heavy nonstick skillet over medium heat. Place pork chops in skillet; brown 2 minutes per side. Reduce heat to low. Cover; cook 15 to 20 minutes, turning occasionally, until internal temperature of chops reaches 160°F.

2. Place apple, shallots and butter in another large nonstick skillet. Cook and stir over medium heat 4 to 5 minutes. Add cabbage, sugar substitute, vinegar and lemon juice. Cook and stir until cabbage is wilted and tender. Season to taste with additional salt substitute and black pepper. Serve pork chop with cabbage mixture and applesauce, if desired.   *Makes 3 servings*

Nutrients per Serving: 1 pork chop with 1 cup cabbage mixture

Calories 236	**Fiber** 5g
Fat 10g (sat 2g)	**Cholesterol** 50mg
Protein 22g	**Sodium** 89mg
Carbohydrate 16g	

Exchanges: 1/2 fruit, 2 vegetable, 2-1/2 lean meat, 1 fat

Toasted Ravioli with Fresh Tomato-Basil Salsa

meatless

Quick Recipe   *(Pictured at right)*

> 1 package (9 ounces) refrigerated cheese ravioli
> Nonstick olive oil cooking spray
> 3/4 cup dry bread crumbs
> 2 tablespoons grated Parmesan cheese
> 1 teaspoon dried basil leaves
> 1 teaspoon dried oregano leaves
> 1/4 teaspoon black pepper
> 2 egg whites
> Fresh Tomato-Basil Salsa (recipe follows)

1. Cook ravioli according to package directions, omitting salt. Rinse under cold running water until ravioli are cool; drain well.

2. Preheat oven to 375°F. Spray large nonstick baking sheet with cooking spray.

3. Combine bread crumbs, cheese, basil, oregano and pepper in medium bowl.

4. Beat egg whites lightly in shallow dish. Add ravioli; toss lightly to coat. Transfer ravioli, a few at a time, to crumb mixture; toss to coat evenly. Arrange on prepared baking sheet. Repeat with remaining ravioli. Spray tops of ravioli with cooking spray. Bake 12 to 14 minutes or until crisp. Meanwhile, prepare Fresh Tomato-Basil Salsa; serve with ravioli. *Makes 8 servings*

Fresh Tomato-Basil Salsa

> 1 pound fresh tomatoes, peeled and seeded
> 1/2 cup loosely packed fresh basil leaves
> 1/4 small onion (about 2×1-inch piece)
> 1 teaspoon red wine vinegar
> 1/4 teaspoon salt

Combine ingredients in food processor; cover and process until finely chopped but not smooth. *Makes about 1 cup*

Nutrients per Serving: 6 ravioli with 2 tablespoons salsa

Calories 167	Fiber 1g
Fat 5g (sat 3g)	Cholesterol 29mg
Protein 8g	Sodium 337mg
Carbohydrate 22g	

Exchanges: 1 starch, 1 vegetable, 1 lean meat, 1/2 fat

ぶ ぶ ぶ

Hurry-Up Tortilla Pizzas

meatless

Quick Recipe

> 8 (6-inch) corn tortillas
> 1 teaspoon ground cumin
> 1-1/2 cups shredded reduced-fat Cheddar or mozzarella cheese
> 1 can (4 ounces) diced mild green chilies, drained
> 1 cup diced seeded fresh tomatoes
> 1/4 cup chopped fresh cilantro

1. Preheat oven to 475°F.

2. Arrange tortillas on large nonstick baking sheet. Sprinkle with cumin. Top with cheese, chilies and tomatoes.

3. Bake 5 minutes or until cheese is melted and tortilla edges are golden. Sprinkle cilantro over pizzas before serving. *Makes 4 servings*

Note: If a large baking sheet is not available, coat a sheet of foil with nonstick cooking spray and line an oven rack with foil. Arrange the tortillas on the foil and proceed with the recipe as instructed.

Nutrients per Serving: 2 tortilla pizzas

Calories 209	Fiber 4g
Fat 4g (sat 2g)	Cholesterol 9mg
Protein 14g	Sodium 459mg
Carbohydrate 29g	

Exchanges: 1-1/2 starch, 1 vegetable, 1-1/2 lean meat

Toasted Ravioli with Fresh Tomato-Basil Salsa

Herbed Shrimp and Mushrooms with Fettuccine

Quick Recipe   *(Pictured at right)*

6 ounces uncooked spinach fettuccine
4 teaspoons olive oil
2 cups sliced fresh mushrooms
1/2 cup chopped onion
1 to 2 cloves garlic, minced
2 teaspoons cornstarch
2/3 cup fat-free reduced-sodium chicken broth
1/2 teaspoon dried rosemary, crushed
1/4 teaspoon salt
1/4 teaspoon black pepper
1 pound fresh or thawed frozen uncooked large shrimp, peeled and deveined
1 large tomato, seeded and chopped
1/4 cup slivered fresh basil
1/4 cup finely shredded Asiago or Parmesan cheese

1. Cook pasta according to package directions, omitting salt. Drain. Keep warm.

2. Heat oil in large skillet over medium heat until hot. Add mushrooms, onion and garlic; cook and stir 5 minutes or until onion is tender.

3. Combine cornstarch, broth, rosemary, salt and pepper in small bowl. Add to mushroom mixture. Bring to a boil, stirring constantly.

4. Add shrimp to skillet; return to a boil. Reduce heat; simmer, covered, 1 to 3 minutes or just until shrimp turn opaque. Stir in tomato and basil.

5. Toss shrimp mixture with pasta. Sprinkle with cheese.   *Makes 6 servings*

Nutrients per Serving: 1-1/3 cups

Calories 225	**Fiber** 2g
Fat 7g (sat 2g)	**Cholesterol** 119mg
Protein 21g	**Sodium** 365mg
Carbohydrate 21g	

Exchanges: 1 starch, 1 vegetable, 2-1/2 lean meat

Chicken & Dumplings Casserole

low fat

3/4 pound chicken tenders, cut into bite-size pieces
6 baby potatoes (red or Yukon gold) (about 1/2 pound), quartered
1 cup baby carrots
1 cup frozen green peas, thawed
2 tablespoons all-purpose flour
1/4 teaspoon salt
1/4 teaspoon black pepper
1 can (14 ounces) fat-free reduced-sodium chicken broth
1/2 cup reduced-fat biscuit baking mix
1/4 cup water

1. Lightly spray 9-inch glass microwavable pie plate with nonstick cooking spray.

2. Place chicken, potatoes, carrots, peas, flour, salt and pepper in large resealable plastic bag. Seal and shake to coat ingredients with flour and seasonings. Empty chicken and vegetables into pie plate, shaking to distribute evenly. Add chicken broth. Cover with 10-inch circle of waxed paper. Microwave at HIGH 20 minutes.

3. Combine biscuit mix and water in bowl; mix lightly with fork. Set aside.

4. Preheat oven to 400°F.

5. Remove pie plate from microwave. Remove and discard waxed paper. Drop teaspoonfuls of biscuit dough over chicken and vegetables. Bake in oven 10 minutes or until dumplings are puffed and cooked through. Remove from oven; let cool 5 minutes before serving.   *Makes 6 servings*

Nutrients per Serving: 1 cup casserole

Calories 231	**Fiber** 4g
Fat 2g (sat <1g)	**Cholesterol** 40mg
Protein 20g	**Sodium** 267mg
Carbohydrate 32g	

Exchanges: 2 starch, 1/2 vegetable, 2 lean meat

Herbed Shrimp and Mushrooms with Fettuccine

Chicken & Broccoli Stir-Fry with Peanuts

Quick Recipe

- 1-1/2 tablespoons cornstarch
- 1-1/2 cups fat-free reduced-sodium chicken broth, divided
- 2 tablespoons reduced-sodium soy sauce
- 1/2 teaspoon salt
- 1/4 teaspoon garlic powder
- 1/4 teaspoon ground ginger
- 1/2 teaspoon canola oil
- 1 pound boneless skinless chicken breasts, cut into 2×1/4-inch strips
- 1 cup small broccoli florets
- 1 cup red bell pepper strips
- 1/4 cup chopped unsalted dry-roasted peanuts

1. Combine cornstarch, 1 cup chicken broth, soy sauce, salt, garlic powder and ginger in small container; stir until smooth. Set aside.

2. Lightly spray large skillet with nonstick cooking spray; heat over high heat until hot. Add oil; tilt skillet to coat bottom. Add chicken; stir-fry 2 minutes or until no longer pink. Remove chicken from skillet.

3. Add remaining 1/2 cup chicken broth to skillet; bring to a boil. Add broccoli and bell pepper; return to a boil. Reduce heat and simmer, covered, 2 minutes or until broccoli is crisp-tender.

4. Increase heat to high. Add chicken to skillet. Stir reserved sauce and add to skillet. Bring to a boil; boil 1 to 2 minutes or until thickened. Stir in peanuts. *Makes 4 servings*

Nutrients per Serving: 1 cup stir-fry

Calories 231	**Fiber** 2g
Fat 8g (sat 2g)	**Cholesterol** 69mg
Protein 31g	**Sodium** 686mg
Carbohydrate 7g	

Exchanges: 1-1/2 vegetable, 3-1/2 lean meat

Baked Rockfish Veracruz

- 1 teaspoon olive oil
- 1/2 small onion, chopped
- 4 cloves garlic, minced
- 8 ounces fresh tomatoes, seeded and chopped *or* 2 cans (14-1/2 ounces each) whole tomatoes, drained and chopped
- 1/2 medium green bell pepper, cored, seeded and chopped
- 1/2 to 1 jalapeño pepper,* seeded and minced (optional)
- 1 teaspoon dried oregano leaves
- 1/2 teaspoon ground cumin
- 1/4 cup small pimiento-stuffed green olives
- 2 teaspoons drained capers (optional)
- 1 pound skinless rockfish, snapper, halibut or cod fillets
- Hot cooked rice (optional)

*Jalapeno peppers can sting and irritate the skin. Wear rubber gloves when handling peppers and do not touch your eyes. Wash hands after handling peppers.

1. Preheat oven to 375°F. Heat oil in large nonstick skillet over medium-high heat. Add onion and garlic. Cook and stir 3 minutes or until onion is tender. Add tomatoes, bell pepper, jalapeño pepper, if desired, oregano and cumin. Cook over high heat, stirring occasionally, 2 to 3 minutes. Stir in olives and capers, if desired. Set aside.

2. Spray 11×7-inch baking dish with nonstick cooking spray. Place fish in single layer in dish, folding thin tail sections under to make fish evenly thick. Pour tomato mixture over fish. Cover with foil; bake 25 minutes or until fish is opaque and flakes when tested with fork. Serve with rice, if desired. *Makes 4 servings*

Nutrients per Serving: 1 fillet with 1/2 cup tomato mixture

Calories 153	**Fiber** 2g
Fat 4g (sat 1g)	**Cholesterol** 39mg
Protein 22g	**Sodium** 347mg
Carbohydrate 6g	

Exchanges: 1 vegetable, 2-1/2 lean meat

Salmon and Crab Cakes

low carb

Quick Recipe

   1/2 pound cooked salmon
   1/2 pound cooked crabmeat (lump crabmeat is best)
     1 beaten egg *or* 1/4 cup egg substitute
1-1/2 tablespoons reduced-fat mayonnaise
     1 tablespoon minced fresh parsley
     1 teaspoon dried dill weed
   1/2 teaspoon salt substitute
   1/2 teaspoon black pepper
   1/2 teaspoon prepared yellow mustard
   1/4 teaspoon Worcestershire sauce
   1/4 cup dry bread crumbs

1. Flake salmon and crabmeat together in medium bowl. Add egg, mayonnaise, parsley, dill, salt substitute, pepper, mustard and Worcestershire sauce. Mix well.

2. Place bread crumbs on shallow rimmed plate. Drop heaping 1/3 cup fish mixture into bread crumbs; shape into thick patty. Repeat with remaining mixture.

3. Spray large nonstick skillet with nonstick cooking spray; heat over medium heat. Place patties in single layer in skillet. Cover; cook fish cakes 5 to 8 minutes, turning once.

Makes 4 servings

Nutrients per Serving: 1 fish cake

Calories 175	**Fiber** <1g
Fat 6g (sat <1g)	**Cholesterol** 114mg
Protein 24g	**Sodium** 739mg
Carbohydrate 5g	

Exchanges: 3 lean meat

Tip

To make dry bread crumbs, bake cubed stale bread on a baking sheet in a 325°F oven until it is very dry and lightly browned. Use a food processor or blender to grind the cubes into fine crumbs.

Harvest Chicken

Quick Recipe   *(Pictured below)*

     1 can (10-3/4 ounces) reduced-fat condensed cream of chicken soup, undiluted
   1/2 cup fat-free milk
   3/4 teaspoon dried Italian seasoning
   1/4 teaspoon dried thyme leaves
     4 boneless skinless chicken breast halves (about 1/4 pound each)
     2 medium red or green apples, cored and sliced
     1 small onion, thinly sliced into rings

1. Combine soup, milk, Italian seasoning and thyme in small bowl; set aside.

2. Spray large nonstick skillet with nonstick cooking spray. Heat over medium heat 1 minute. Add chicken; cook 5 minutes per side or until browned. Remove from skillet; set aside.

3. Add apples and onion to skillet. Cook until onion is tender. Stir in reserved soup mixture and chicken. Reduce heat to low. Cover; simmer 5 to 10 minutes or until chicken is no longer pink in center.

Makes 4 servings

Nutrients per Serving: 1 chicken breast with about 1 cup apple and onion mixture

Calories 246	**Fiber** 3g
Fat 6g (sat 2g)	**Cholesterol** 79mg
Protein 29g	**Sodium** 681mg
Carbohydrate 20g	

Exchanges: 1/2 starch, 1 fruit, 3 lean meat

Harvest Chicken

Cavatelli and Vegetable Stir-Fry

low fat · meatless

Quick Recipe (Pictured at right)

3/4 cup uncooked cavatelli or elbow
    macaroni

6 ounces fresh snow peas, cut lengthwise
    into halves

1/2 cup thinly sliced carrot

1 teaspoon minced fresh gingerroot

1/2 cup chopped yellow or green bell
    pepper

1/2 cup chopped onion

1/4 cup chopped fresh parsley

1 tablespoon chopped fresh oregano *or*
    1 teaspoon dried oregano leaves,
    crushed

1 tablespoon reduced-fat butter

2 tablespoons water

1 tablespoon reduced-sodium soy sauce

1. Prepare pasta according to package
directions, omitting salt; drain and set aside.

2. Spray wok or large nonstick skillet with
nonstick cooking spray. Add snow peas,
carrot and gingerroot; stir-fry 2 minutes over
medium-high heat. Add bell pepper, onion,
parsley, oregano and butter. Stir-fry 2 to
3 minutes or until vegetables are crisp-tender.
Stir in water and soy sauce. Stir in pasta; heat
through. Makes 4 servings

Nutrients per Serving: 1 cup stir-fry

Calories 125	**Fiber** 3g
Fat 2g (sat <1g)	**Cholesterol** 4mg
Protein 5g	**Sodium** 171mg
Carbohydrate 23g	

Exchanges: 1 starch, 1-1/2 vegetable, 1/2 fat

Browned Pork Chops with Gravy

Quick Recipe

1/2 teaspoon dried sage leaves

1/2 teaspoon dried marjoram leaves

1/4 teaspoon black pepper

1/8 teaspoon salt

4 boneless pork loin chops (about
    1/4 pound each), trimmed of fat

1/4 cup coarsely chopped onion

1 clove garlic, minced

1 cup sliced fresh mushrooms

3/4 cup beef broth

1/3 cup fat-free sour cream

1 tablespoon all-purpose flour

1 teaspoon Dijon mustard

2 cups hot cooked wide noodles

1. Combine sage, marjoram, pepper and salt in
small bowl. Rub onto both sides of chops. Spray
large nonstick skillet with nonstick cooking
spray; heat over medium heat. Place chops in
skillet. Cook 5 minutes, turning once, or until
chops are just barely pink. Remove chops from
skillet; keep warm.

2. Add onion and garlic to skillet; cook and stir
2 minutes. Add mushrooms and broth. Bring to
a boil. Reduce heat and simmer, covered, 3 to
4 minutes or until mushrooms are tender.

3. Whisk together sour cream, flour and mustard
in medium bowl. Whisk in about 3 tablespoons
broth from skillet. Stir sour cream mixture into
skillet. Cook, stirring constantly, until mixture
comes to a boil. Serve over pork chops and
noodles. *Makes 4 servings*

Nutrients per Serving: 1 pork chop with 1/2 cup
noodles and about 1/3 cup gravy

Calories 278	**Fiber** 1g
Fat 7g (sat 2g)	**Cholesterol** 78mg
Protein 26g	**Sodium** 324mg
Carbohydrate 27g	

Exchanges: 1-1/2 starch, 1/2 vegetable, 3 lean meat

Cavatelli and Vegetable Stir-Fry

Tex-Mex Tostadas

Quick Recipe

4 (7-inch) fat-free flour tortillas
Nonstick cooking spray
1 medium green bell pepper, diced
3/4 pound boneless skinless chicken breasts, cut into strips
1-1/2 teaspoons minced garlic
1 teaspoon chili powder
1 teaspoon ground cumin
1/2 cup prepared chunky salsa, divided
1/3 cup sliced green onions
1 cup fat-free refried beans
1 medium fresh tomato, diced
1/4 cup fat-free or reduced-fat sour cream (optional)

1. Preheat oven to 450°F. Place tortillas on baking sheet; coat both sides with cooking spray. Bake 5 minutes or until lightly browned and crisp. Remove; set aside.

2. Meanwhile, spray large nonstick skillet with cooking spray. Add bell pepper; cook and stir 4 minutes. Add chicken, garlic, chili powder and cumin; cook and stir 4 minutes or until chicken is no longer pink in center. Add 1/4 cup salsa and green onions; cook and stir 1 minute. Remove skillet from heat; set aside.

3. Combine refried beans and remaining 1/4 cup salsa in microwavable bowl. Cook, uncovered, at HIGH 1-1/2 minutes or until beans are heated through.

4. Spread bean mixture evenly over tortillas. Spoon chicken mixture and tomato over bean mixture. Top with sour cream, if desired.

Makes 4 servings

Nutrients per Serving: 1 tostada

Calories 251	**Fiber** 11g
Fat 3g (sat 1g)	**Cholesterol** 52mg
Protein 26g	**Sodium** 707mg
Carbohydrate 30g	

Exchanges: 1-1/2 starch, 1-1/2 vegetable, 2 lean meat

Chicken Primavera Buffet

8 ounces uncooked thin spaghetti
1/4 cup prepared pesto
1/4 cup prepared fat-free Italian salad dressing
1/2 teaspoon dried red pepper flakes
2 cups water
1 cup thinly sliced carrots
1 cup broccoli florets
1 cup snow peas
1 can (4 ounces) sliced water chestnuts, drained
8 boneless skinless chicken breast halves (about 1/4 pound each)

1. Preheat oven to 350°F. Spray 13×9-inch baking dish with nonstick cooking spray. Cook pasta according to package directions, omitting salt. Drain and rinse well under cold water until pasta is cool; drain well. Place in large bowl; set aside.

2. Combine pesto, Italian dressing and red pepper flakes in small bowl. Reserve 1 tablespoon pesto mixture. Add remaining pesto mixture to pasta; toss to coat well.

3. Bring water to a boil over high heat in large saucepan. Add carrots, broccoli and snow peas; cook 3 minutes. Drain vegetables. Add water chestnuts and vegetables to pasta; toss to blend well. Transfer pasta and vegetables to prepared dish.

4. Spray large nonstick skillet with cooking spray; heat over medium heat until hot. Add chicken; cook until browned on both sides. Cover; cook 10 minutes or until no longer pink in center and juices run clear. Place chicken on pasta and vegetables. Pour juices from skillet over chicken. Spread reserved 1 tablespoon pesto mixture over chicken. Bake 45 minutes or until heated through.   *Makes 8 servings*

Nutrients per Serving: 1 chicken breast half with 3/4 cup pasta mixture

Calories 224	**Fiber** 2g
Fat 3g (sat 1g)	**Cholesterol** 45mg
Protein 22g	**Sodium** 190mg
Carbohydrate 26g	

Exchanges: 1-1/2 starch, 1 vegetable, 2-1/2 lean meat

Mustard-Crusted Roast Pork Tenderloin & Vegetables

Mustard-Crusted Roast Pork Tenderloin & Vegetables

low carb

(Pictured above)

3 tablespoons Dijon mustard

4 teaspoons minced garlic, divided

2 pork tenderloins (about 1 pound each)

2 tablespoons dried thyme leaves

1 teaspoon black pepper

1/2 teaspoon salt

1 bunch (about 1 pound) fresh asparagus spears, ends trimmed

2 medium red or yellow bell peppers (or one of each), cored, seeded and cut lengthwise into 1/2-inch-thick strips

1 cup fat-free reduced-sodium chicken broth, divided

1. Preheat oven to 375°F. Combine mustard and 3 teaspoons garlic in small bowl. Place tenderloins on waxed paper; spread mustard mixture evenly over top and sides of both tenderloins.

2. Combine thyme, black pepper and salt in small bowl; reserve 1 teaspoon mixture. Sprinkle remaining mixture evenly over tenderloins, patting so that seasoning adheres to mustard. Place tenderloins on rack in shallow roasting pan. Roast 25 minutes.

3. Arrange asparagus and bell peppers in single layer in shallow casserole or 13×9-inch baking dish. Add 1/4 cup broth, reserved 1 teaspoon thyme mixture and remaining 1 teaspoon garlic; toss to coat.

4. Roast vegetables in oven, alongside pork tenderloins, 15 to 20 minutes or until thermometer inserted into center of pork registers 160°F and vegetables are tender. Transfer tenderloins to carving board; tent with foil and let stand 5 minutes. Arrange vegetables on serving platter, reserving juices; cover vegetables and keep warm. Add remaining 3/4 cup broth and vegetable juices to roasting dish, scraping up any browned bits. Transfer to small saucepan. Simmer 3 to 4 minutes over medium-high heat or until juices are reduced to 3/4 cup, stirring frequently. Carve tenderloin crosswise into 1/4-inch-thick slices; arrange on serving platter. Spoon juices over tenderloin and vegetables. *Makes 8 servings*

Nutrients per Serving: 1/8 of pork (about 3 ounces cooked weight) with about 1/2 cup vegetables and 1-1/2 tablespoons juices

Calories 182	**Fiber** 1g
Fat 5g (sat 2g)	**Cholesterol** 65mg
Protein 27g	**Sodium** 304mg
Carbohydrate 8g	

Exchanges: 1-1/2 vegetable, 3 lean meat

Tip

Prevent unnecessary foodborne illnesses. Always cook meat and poultry to the safe internal temperatures given in recipes. Use a meat thermometer to check for doneness.

Beef Pot Roast

Beef Pot Roast

(Pictured above)

1 beef eye of round roast (about 2-1/2 pounds), trimmed of fat

1 can (14 ounces) reduced-sodium beef broth

2 cloves garlic

1 teaspoon herbs de Provence *or* 1/4 teaspoon *each* dried thyme, sage, savory and rosemary, crushed

4 small turnips, peeled and cut into wedges

10 ounces fresh brussels sprouts (about 10 medium), trimmed

8 ounces baby carrots (about 2 cups)

4 ounces pearl onions (about 1 cup), skins removed

2 teaspoons cornstarch

1 tablespoon water

1. Heat Dutch oven over medium-high heat. Brown roast evenly on all sides.

2. Pour broth into Dutch oven; bring to a boil over high heat. Add garlic and herbs de Provence. Cover and reduce heat; simmer 1-1/2 hours.

3. Add turnips, brussels sprouts, carrots and onions to Dutch oven. Cover; cook 25 to 30 minutes or until vegetables are tender. Remove meat and vegetables and arrange on serving platter; cover with foil to keep warm.

4. Strain broth; return to Dutch oven. Stir cornstarch into water in small bowl until smooth. Stir cornstarch mixture into broth. Bring to a boil over medium-high heat; cook and stir 1 minute or until thick and bubbly. Serve gravy immediately with pot roast and vegetables.

Makes 8 servings

Nutrients per Serving: 1/8 of beef (about 3-3/4 ounces cooked weight) with 3/4 cup vegetables and 1/4 cup gravy

Calories 261	**Fiber** 2g
Fat 9g (sat 3g)	**Cholesterol** 79mg
Protein 35g	**Sodium** 142mg
Carbohydrate 11g	

Exchanges: 2 vegetable, 4 lean meat

Soy-Sherry Pork Chop Casserole

Quick Recipe

>   4 boneless pork chops (about 5 ounces each), trimmed of fat
>   1 medium onion, sliced
>   1 medium green bell pepper, cored, seeded and sliced
>   3/4 cup water
>   1/2 (8-ounce) can sliced water chestnuts, drained
>   1/2 cup uncooked instant rice
>   1 teaspoon reduced-sodium beef bouillon granules
>   2 tablespoons reduced-sodium soy sauce
>   2 tablespoons dry sherry or unsweetened apple juice
>   1 tablespoon sugar substitute*
>   1/4 teaspoon ground ginger
>   1/8 teaspoon dried red pepper flakes (optional)

*This recipe was tested with SPLENDA® Granular.

1. Spray large nonstick skillet with nonstick cooking spray; heat over medium-high heat until hot. Add pork chops; cook 4 to 5 minutes or until browned on both sides. Remove from skillet. Set aside. (Do not drain skillet.)

2. Add onion, bell pepper, water, water chestnuts, rice and bouillon granules to drippings in skillet; stir to blend. Bring mixture to a boil. Top with pork chops. Cover tightly; simmer 10 minutes or until pork is no longer pink in center.

3. Meanwhile, combine remaining ingredients in small bowl; set aside.

4. Remove skillet from heat. Spoon 1 tablespoon soy sauce mixture evenly over each serving.

Makes 4 servings

Nutrients per Serving: 1 pork chop with 3/4 cup vegetable and rice mixture and 1 tablespoon soy sauce mixture

Calories 297	**Fiber** 3g
Fat 8g (sat 3g)	**Cholesterol** 84mg
Protein 33g	**Sodium** 464mg
Carbohydrate 22g	

Exchanges: 1 starch, 1-1/2 vegetable, 4 lean meat

Beef Stroganoff

Quick Recipe

>   1 boneless beef top sirloin steak (about 1 pound), trimmed of fat
>   1 large onion, cut lengthwise in half and thinly sliced
>   1/2 cup plain fat-free yogurt
>   1/2 cup reduced-fat sour cream
>   3 tablespoons snipped chives, divided
>   2 tablespoons all-purpose flour
>   1 tablespoon ketchup
>   2 teaspoons Dijon mustard
>   1/4 teaspoon salt
>   1/8 teaspoon white pepper
>   1 teaspoon olive oil
>   6 ounces portobello or button mushrooms, sliced
>   3 cups hot cooked wide noodles
>   12 ounces baby carrots, steamed

1. Cut beef in half lengthwise, then crosswise into 1/4-inch slices; set aside.

2. Spray large nonstick skillet with nonstick cooking spray. Heat over low heat. Add onion. Cover; cook, stirring occasionally, 10 minutes or until tender. Remove onion from skillet; set aside.

3. Combine yogurt, sour cream, 2 tablespoons chives, flour, ketchup, mustard, salt and pepper in small bowl; set aside.

4. Heat oil in same skillet over medium-high heat. Add beef and mushrooms; cook and stir 3 to 4 minutes or until beef is lightly browned. Return onion to skillet. Reduce heat to low. Stir in yogurt mixture until well blended and slightly thickened, about 2 minutes. Serve over noodles with carrots. Sprinkle with remaining 1 tablespoon chives.

Makes 6 servings

Nutrients per Serving: 1/2 cup noodles with 1/2 cup beef mixture and 1/2 cup cooked carrots

Calories 301	**Fiber** 3g
Fat 7g (sat 3g)	**Cholesterol** 79mg
Protein 24g	**Sodium** 282mg
Carbohydrate 33g	

Exchanges: 2 starch, 1 vegetable, 2 lean meat

Sides & Salads

Asparagus with No-Cook Creamy Mustard Sauce

Quick Recipe (Pictured at left)

> **1/2 cup plain fat-free yogurt**
> **2 tablespoons reduced-fat mayonnaise**
> **1 tablespoon Dijon mustard**
> **2 teaspoons lemon juice**
> **1/2 teaspoon salt**
> **2 cups water**
> **1-1/2 pounds fresh asparagus spears, rinsed and ends trimmed**
> **Black pepper to taste**

1. For sauce, combine yogurt, mayonnaise, mustard, lemon juice and salt in small bowl. Whisk until smooth; set aside.

2. Bring water to a boil in large skillet over high heat. Add asparagus. Return to a boil. Reduce heat. Cover tightly; simmer 3 minutes or until just crisp-tender. Remove from water; drain on paper towels.

3. Place asparagus on serving platter and spoon sauce over top. Sprinkle with black pepper. *Makes 6 servings*

Nutrients per Serving: about 6 spears with 2 tablespoons sauce

Calories 57	**Fiber** 2g
Fat 2g (sat <1g)	**Cholesterol** 2mg
Protein 4g	**Sodium** 299mg
Carbohydrate 8g	

Exchanges: 1-1/2 vegetable, 1/2 fat

Clockwise from top left: *Sweet and Sour Carrots (page 112), Rice Pilaf with Dried Cherries and Almonds (page 122), Asparagus with No-Cook Creamy Mustard Sauce, and Italian Crouton Salad (page 106)*

105

Sensational Spinach Salad with Orange Poppy Seed Vinaigrette

low fat   meatless

Quick Recipe   *(Pictured at right)*

1/4 cup orange juice
3 tablespoons red wine vinegar
2 tablespoons sugar
1 tablespoon olive oil
1 teaspoon grated orange peel
1 teaspoon poppy seeds
1/4 teaspoon salt
9 cups washed and stemmed spinach leaves
1 can (15 ounces) chilled mandarin orange segments, drained
1-1/2 cups sliced fresh mushrooms
1 small red onion, sliced and separated into rings
3 cooked egg whites, coarsely chopped

1. To prepare vinaigrette, combine orange juice, red wine vinegar, sugar, olive oil, orange peel, poppy seeds and salt in small bowl until well blended; set aside.

2. To prepare salad, combine spinach, orange segments, mushrooms, onion and egg whites in large serving bowl.

3. Pour vinaigrette over spinach mixture just before serving; toss to coat. Serve immediately.

Makes 6 servings

Nutrients per Serving: 2-1/2 cups salad with about 1-1/2 tablespoons vinaigrette

Calories 106	**Fiber** 3g
Fat 3g (sat <1g)	**Cholesterol** 0mg
Protein 5g	**Sodium** 196mg
Carbohydrate 17g	

Exchanges: 1/2 fruit, 2 vegetable, 1/2 fat

Italian Crouton Salad

meatless

(Pictured on page 104)

6 ounces French or Italian bread
1/4 cup plain fat-free yogurt
1/4 cup red wine vinegar
4 teaspoons olive oil
1 tablespoon water
3 cloves garlic, minced
6 medium plum tomatoes (about 12 ounces)
1/2 medium red onion, thinly sliced
3 tablespoons slivered fresh basil
2 tablespoons finely chopped fresh parsley
12 red leaf lettuce leaves *or* 4 cups prepared Italian salad mix
2 tablespoons shredded Parmesan cheese

1. Preheat broiler. To prepare croutons, cut bread into 3/4-inch cubes. Place in single layer on baking sheet. Broil 4 inches from heat 3 minutes or until bread is golden, stirring every 30 seconds to 1 minute. Remove from baking sheet; place in large bowl.

2. Whisk together yogurt, vinegar, oil, water and garlic in small bowl until blended; set aside. Core tomatoes; cut into 1/4-inch-thick slices. Add to croutons along with onion, basil and parsley; stir until blended. Pour yogurt mixture over crouton mixture; toss to coat. Cover; refrigerate 30 minutes or up to 1 day. (Croutons will be more tender the following day.)

3. To serve, place lettuce on plates. Spoon crouton mixture over lettuce. Top with Parmesan cheese.

Makes 6 servings

Nutrients per Serving: about 1-1/3 cups crouton mixture with 2 lettuce leaves and 1 teaspoon cheese

Calories 160	**Fiber** 2g
Fat 5g (sat 1g)	**Cholesterol** 2mg
Protein 6g	**Sodium** 234mg
Carbohydrate 25g	

Exchanges: 1 starch, 2 vegetable, 1 fat

Sensational Spinach Salad with Orange Poppy Seed Vinaigrette

Cranberry-Apple Gelatin Salad

(Pictured at right)

**2 packages (4-serving size each)
sugar-free cranberry-flavored gelatin***
1-1/2 cups boiling water
2 cups diet lemon-lime-flavored soda
1 cup finely chopped red apple
1/2 cup finely chopped celery
3 tablespoons finely chopped walnuts

*Any red-colored sugar-free gelatin can be used.

1. Dissolve gelatin in boiling water in medium bowl. Refrigerate 15 minutes. Stir in soda. Cover; chill 1 to 1-1/2 hours or until partially set.

2. Fold in apple, celery and walnuts. Pour into 6-cup gelatin mold or 12 (6-ounce) custard cups. Cover; refrigerate at least 4 hours or until set. If using gelatin mold, remove from mold.

Makes 12 servings

Nutrients per Serving: 1/2 cup salad

Calories 28	**Fiber** 1g
Fat 1g (sat <1g)	**Cholesterol** 0mg
Protein 1g	**Sodium** 58mg
Carbohydrate 3g	

Exchanges: Free

Mediterranean Tuna Salad

1 cup diced fresh tomato
1 tablespoon lemon juice
1 tablespoon olive oil
2 teaspoons Dijon mustard
1 large clove garlic, minced
1/4 teaspoon salt
1/4 teaspoon dried basil leaves
**2 cans (6 ounces each) solid white tuna
packed in water, drained and flaked**
1/2 cup diced celery
1/3 cup chopped fresh basil
Red leaf lettuce leaves
1/2 pound fresh green beans, steamed
**1 medium red bell pepper, cored, seeded
and cut into strips**
8 cherry tomatoes, cut into halves

1. Combine diced tomato, lemon juice, oil, mustard, garlic, salt and dried basil in large bowl; let stand 5 minutes. Stir in tuna, celery and fresh basil. Refrigerate, covered, 1 to 2 hours to allow flavors to blend, stirring once.

2. Line serving platter with lettuce leaves. Mound tuna salad in center; surround with green beans, bell pepper and cherry tomatoes.

Makes 4 servings

Nutrients per Serving: about 3/4 cup tuna salad with 1/3 cup green beans, 1/4 of red bell pepper and 2 cherry tomatoes

Calories 194	**Fiber** 2g
Fat 5g (sat 1g)	**Cholesterol** 16mg
Protein 28g	**Sodium** 507mg
Carbohydrate 11g	

Exchanges: 2 vegetable, 3 lean meat

Cranberry-Apple Gelatin Salad

Mediterranean Orzo
and Vegetable Pilaf

Quick Recipe   (Pictured at right)

**1/2 cup plus 2 tablespoons (4 ounces)
uncooked orzo pasta
2 teaspoons olive oil
1 small onion, diced
2 cloves garlic, minced
1 small zucchini, diced
1/2 cup fat-free reduced-sodium chicken
broth
1 can (14 ounces) artichoke hearts,
drained and quartered
1 medium fresh tomato, chopped
1/2 teaspoon dried oregano leaves
1/2 teaspoon salt
1/4 teaspoon black pepper
1/2 cup crumbled feta cheese
Sliced ripe olives (optional)**

1. Cook orzo according to package directions,
omitting salt. Drain. Keep warm.

2. Meanwhile, heat olive oil in large nonstick
skillet over medium-high heat. Add onion; cook
about 5 minutes or until tender, stirring
occasionally. Add garlic; cook and stir 1 minute.

3. Add zucchini and chicken broth to skillet.
Reduce heat; simmer about 5 minutes or until
zucchini is crisp-tender.

4. Add orzo, artichoke hearts, tomato, oregano,
salt and pepper to skillet; cook, stirring constantly,
about 1 minute or until just heated through.
Sprinkle with feta cheese. Top with olive slices,
if desired.   *Makes 6 servings*

Nutrients per Serving: 1/2 cup pilaf

Calories 168	**Fiber** 3g
Fat 7g (sat 2g)	**Cholesterol** 11mg
Protein 7g	**Sodium** 516mg
Carbohydrate 23g	

Exchanges: 1 starch, 1-1/2 vegetable, 1/2 lean meat,
1/2 fat

Toasted Peanut
Couscous Salad

meatless

Quick Recipe

**1/2 cup water
1/4 cup uncooked quick-cooking couscous
1 ounce (about 3 tablespoons) unsalted
dry-roasted peanuts
1/2 cup finely chopped red onion
1/2 cup finely chopped green bell pepper
1 tablespoon reduced-sodium soy sauce
2 teaspoons cider vinegar
1-1/2 teaspoons dark sesame oil
1/2 teaspoon grated fresh gingerroot
1 packet sugar substitute*
1/4 teaspoon salt
1/8 teaspoon dried red pepper flakes**

*This recipe was tested with SPLENDA® Packets.

1. Bring water to a boil in small saucepan over
high heat. Remove from heat; stir in couscous.
Cover tightly; let stand 5 minutes or until water
is absorbed. Remove from pan to cool quickly, if
desired.

2. Heat small nonstick skillet over medium-high
heat until hot. Add nuts; cook 2 to 3 minutes or
until beginning to turn golden, stirring
frequently.

3. Combine remaining ingredients in medium
bowl. Add cooled couscous and toasted nuts;
toss gently to blend.   *Makes 4 servings*

Nutrients per Serving: 1/2 cup salad

Calories 115	**Fiber** 2g
Fat 5g (sat 1g)	**Cholesterol** 0mg
Protein 4g	**Sodium** 298mg
Carbohydrate 14g	

Exchanges: 1 starch, 1 fat

*Mediterranean Orzo and
Vegetable Pilaf*

Tangy Apple Slaw

Tangy Apple Slaw

meatless

(Pictured above)

4 cups shredded green cabbage
1 cup shredded carrots
1 cup chopped unpeeled apple (1 medium)
**1/2 cup thinly sliced red or green bell
    pepper strips**
2/3 cup light mayonnaise or salad dressing
1/3 cup reduced-fat sour cream
3 tablespoons EQUAL® SPOONFUL*
1-1/2 tablespoons Dijon mustard
1 tablespoon lemon juice
1/8 teaspoon pepper

*May substitute 4-1/2 packets EQUAL® sweetener.

• Combine cabbage, carrots, apple and bell
pepper in medium bowl. Mix mayonnaise, sour
cream, Equal®, mustard, lemon juice and
pepper in small bowl; stir until well blended.
Spoon Equal® mixture over cabbage mixture;
gently toss to combine. Refrigerate, covered,
1 to 2 hours to allow flavors to blend.

Makes 6 servings

Nutrients per Serving: 3/4 cup slaw

Calories 152	**Fiber** 2g
Fat 11g (sat 2g)	**Cholesterol** 15mg
Protein 2g	**Sodium** 331mg
Carbohydrate 13g	

Exchanges: 2 vegetable, 2 fat

ৡ ৡ ৡ

Sweet and Sour Carrots

meatless

Quick Recipe   (Pictured on page 104)

2 cups carrot slices, 1/4 inch thick
1/2 cup celery slices, 1/2 inch thick
**1 can (8 ounces) pineapple tidbits (drain
    and reserve juice)**
1 tablespoon vinegar
2 teaspoons cornstarch
1 teaspoon light soy sauce
1/8 teaspoon salt
2 tablespoons stick butter or margarine
1/4 cup sliced green onions
1/4 cup EQUAL® SPOONFUL*

*May substitute 6 packets EQUAL® sweetener.

• Cook carrots and celery in medium saucepan
in small amount of water about 8 minutes or
until tender. Drain and set aside.

• Add enough water to reserved pineapple
juice to make 1/2 cup liquid. Stir in vinegar,
cornstarch, soy sauce and salt. Cook in medium
saucepan until liquid thickens.

• Add butter, drained pineapple and green
onions; cook and stir until heated through.
Add drained carrots and celery; cook about
2 minutes or until heated through. Stir in Equal®.

Makes 6 servings

Nutrients per Serving: about 2/3 cup

Calories 80	**Fiber** 2g
Fat 4g (sat 2g)	**Cholesterol** 10mg
Protein 1g	**Sodium** 170mg
Carbohydrate 11g	

Exchanges: 1/2 fruit, 1 vegetable, 1 fat

Light Lemon Cauliflower

Quick Recipe   (Pictured at bottom right)

1/4 cup chopped fresh parsley, divided
1/2 teaspoon grated lemon peel
6 cups cauliflower florets (about
    1-1/2 pounds)
1 tablespoon reduced-fat butter
3 cloves garlic, minced
2 tablespoons fresh lemon juice
1/4 cup shredded Parmesan cheese

1. Place 1 tablespoon parsley, lemon peel and about 1 inch of water in large saucepan. Place cauliflower in steamer basket and place in saucepan. Bring water to a boil over medium heat. Cover and steam cauliflower 14 to 16 minutes or until crisp-tender. Remove to large bowl; keep warm. Reserve 1/2 cup hot liquid.

2. Heat butter in small saucepan over medium heat. Add garlic; cook and stir 2 to 3 minutes or until soft. Stir in lemon juice and reserved 1/2 cup liquid.

3. Spoon lemon sauce over cauliflower. Sprinkle with remaining 3 tablespoons parsley and cheese before serving.   *Makes 6 servings*

Nutrients per Serving: about 2/3 cup cauliflower with 1-1/2 tablespoons sauce and 2 teaspoons cheese

Calories 50	**Fiber** 3g
Fat 2g (sat 1g)	**Cholesterol** 6mg
Protein 4g	**Sodium** 113mg
Carbohydrate 6g	

Exchanges: 1 vegetable, 1/2 fat

Green Beans and Garlic

Quick Recipe

2 pounds fresh green beans
2 tablespoons olive oil
3 cloves garlic, minced
1 tablespoon reduced-sodium soy sauce
1/8 teaspoon black pepper

1. Rinse beans, but do not drain or dry. Snap into 2-inch lengths. Set aside.

2. Heat oil in large saucepan over medium heat. Cook garlic 1 to 2 minutes or until aromatic. Add soy sauce and wet beans. Cover and steam, lifting lid to stir occasionally. Steam beans until crisp-tender and bright green, adding small amounts of water if needed. Season with pepper before serving.   *Makes 6 servings*

Nutrients per Serving: 1 cup green beans

Calories 92	**Fiber** 5g
Fat 5g (sat <1g)	**Cholesterol** 0mg
Protein 3g	**Sodium** 93mg
Carbohydrate 11g	

Exchanges: 2 vegetable, 1 fat

Light Lemon Cauliflower

Spaghetti Squash with Black Beans and Zucchini

(Pictured at right)

Nonstick cooking spray
1 small spaghetti squash (about 2 pounds)
2 medium zucchini, cut lengthwise into 1/4-inch-thick slices
2 cups chopped seeded fresh tomatoes
1 can (15 ounces) black beans, rinsed and drained
2 tablespoons chopped fresh basil
2 tablespoons olive oil
2 tablespoons red wine vinegar
1 large clove garlic, minced
1/2 teaspoon salt

1. Spray cold grid of grill with cooking spray. Prepare grill for direct grilling. Pierce spaghetti squash in several places with fork. Wrap in large piece of heavy-duty foil using drugstore wrap technique.* Grill squash on covered grill over medium coals 45 minutes to 1 hour or until easily depressed with back of long-handled spoon, turning a quarter turn every 15 minutes. Remove squash from grill and let stand in foil 10 to 15 minutes.

2. Meanwhile, spray both sides of zucchini slices with cooking spray. Grill on uncovered grill over medium coals 4 minutes or until tender, turning once. Remove from grill. Cut into bite-size pieces.

3. Remove spaghetti squash from foil and cut in half; scoop out seeds. With two forks, separate squash into strands and place on large serving plate. Place tomatoes, beans, zucchini and basil in medium bowl. Combine oil, vinegar, garlic and salt in small bowl; mix thoroughly. Add to vegetables and toss gently to combine. Top spaghetti squash with vegetable mixture.

Makes 4 servings

*Place food in center of oblong piece of heavy-duty foil, leaving at least 2-inch border around food. Bring 2 long sides together above food; fold down in series of locked folds, allowing room for heat circulation and expansion. Fold short ends up and over again. Press folds firmly to seal foil packet.

Nutrients per Serving: 3/4 cup spaghetti squash with 1-1/4 cups vegetable mixture (without French bread)

Calories 219	Fiber 8g
Fat 8g (sat 1g)	Cholesterol 0mg
Protein 12g	Sodium 613mg
Carbohydrate 34g	

Exchanges: 2 starch, 1 vegetable, 1/2 lean meat, 1 fat

✄ ✄ ✄

Bayou Cajun Fries

Quick Recipe

1 baking potato (about 6 ounces), scrubbed
1/2 teaspoon olive oil
1/4 teaspoon paprika
1/4 teaspoon Cajun seasoning
1/8 teaspoon salt

1. Preheat oven to 475°F.

2. To make fries, cut potato lengthwise into 1/4-inch-thick slices, then cut each slice into 1/4-inch-wide strips.

3. Spray nonstick baking sheet with nonstick cooking spray. Place potato on baking sheet; drizzle with oil and sprinkle with paprika. Toss gently to coat.

4. Arrange potato strips in single layer with small amount of space between each strip. Bake 5 minutes. Stir and bake 5 minutes more or until golden brown and tender when pierced with fork.

5. Remove fries from oven. Immediately sprinkle with Cajun seasoning and salt. Toss gently to coat.

Makes 2 servings

Nutrients per Serving: 2/3 cup fries

Calories 91	Fiber 2g
Fat 1g (sat <1g)	Cholesterol 0mg
Protein 2g	Sodium 166mg
Carbohydrate 18g	

Exchanges: 1 starch, 1/2 vegetable

Spaghetti Squash with Black Beans and Zucchini

Herbed Corn on the Cob

Quick Recipe   *(Pictured at right)*

     1 tablespoon butter
     1 teaspoon mixed dried herb leaves, such
         as basil, oregano, sage and rosemary,
         crushed
   1/8 teaspoon salt
         Black pepper
     4 medium ears corn (6 to 7 ounces each),
         husks removed

Microwave Directions

1. Combine butter, herbs, salt and pepper in small microwavable bowl. Microwave at MEDIUM (50%) 30 to 45 seconds or until butter is melted.

2. With pastry brush, coat corn with butter mixture. Place corn on microwavable plate; microwave at HIGH 5 to 6 minutes. Turn corn over and microwave at HIGH 5 to 6 minutes more or until tender.   *Makes 4 servings*

Note: This recipe was tested in an 1100-watt microwave oven.

Nutrients per Serving: 1 ear corn

Calories 86	**Fiber** 2g
Fat 4g (sat 2g)	**Cholesterol** 8mg
Protein 2g	**Sodium** 106mg
Carbohydrate 14g	

Exchanges: 1 starch, 1/2 fat

Tip

The U.S. government released its guidelines for healthy eating earlier this year. Within the guidelines, it is recommended that half of your grain servings come from whole-grain products. The whole wheat macaroni in this macaroni salad is a great way to help you meet that goal.

Country Time Macaroni Salad

Quick Recipe

   1/2 cup (2 ounces) uncooked whole wheat
         or regular elbow macaroni
     3 tablespoons reduced-fat mayonnaise
     2 tablespoons plain fat-free yogurt
     2 teaspoons sweet pickle relish
   3/4 teaspoon dried dill weed
   1/2 teaspoon prepared yellow mustard
         (optional)
   1/4 teaspoon salt
   1/4 pound 99% fat-free ham, cubed
   1/2 cup frozen green peas
   1/2 cup chopped green bell pepper
   1/3 cup thinly sliced celery
     4 tablespoons shredded reduced-fat
         Cheddar cheese, divided

1. Cook pasta according to package directions, omitting salt; drain. Rinse under cold water until completely cooled; drain.

2. Meanwhile, combine mayonnaise, yogurt, relish, dill, mustard, if desired, and salt in small bowl; stir until well blended. Combine ham, peas, bell pepper and celery in medium bowl.

3. Add pasta and mayonnaise mixture to ham mixture; toss gently to coat completely. Add 2 tablespoons cheese; toss lightly. Sprinkle remaining 2 tablespoons cheese over top. Serve immediately.   *Makes 6 servings*

Hint: For the best flavor, prepare the mayonnaise ingredients in a separate bowl at the time of serving.

Nutrients per Serving: 1/2 cup salad

Calories 98	**Fiber** 1g
Fat 3g (sat 1g)	**Cholesterol** 12mg
Protein 7g	**Sodium** 363mg
Carbohydrate 12g	

Exchanges: 1/2 starch, 1/2 vegetable, 1/2 lean meat, 1/2 fat

Warm Roasted Vegetable Salad

Warm Roasted Vegetable Salad

  low fat · meatless

(Pictured above)

4 cups fresh broccoli florets

2 medium red bell peppers, cut into 1/4-inch-thick slices

1 small red onion, cut into 1/4-inch-thick slices

1 small yellow onion, cut into 1/4-inch-thick slices

1-1/2 teaspoons olive oil

1 tablespoon Dijon mustard

1 tablespoon balsamic vinegar

1 teaspoon hot pepper sauce (optional)

1/2 teaspoon salt

1/4 cup slivered fresh basil

1. Preheat oven to 350°F.

2. Combine broccoli, bell peppers, onions and oil in large baking dish; toss to coat. Bake vegetables 25 minutes, stirring occasionally.

3. Meanwhile, combine mustard, vinegar, hot pepper sauce, if desired, and salt in small bowl with wire whisk until smooth. Stir mixture into hot vegetables; toss to coat. Sprinkle salad with basil. Serve warm.   *Makes 6 servings*

Nutrients per Serving: 1-1/2 cups salad

Calories 61	**Fiber** 3g
Fat 2g (sat <1g)	**Cholesterol** 0mg
Protein 2g	**Sodium** 278mg
Carbohydrate 11g	

Exchanges: 2 vegetable, 1/2 fat

Mexicali Bean & Cheese Salad

1 teaspoon canola oil
1 clove garlic, finely chopped
1/4 cup finely chopped red onion
1-1/2 teaspoons chili powder
1/4 teaspoon ground cumin
1/8 teaspoon dried red pepper flakes
1 boneless skinless chicken breast half (about 6 ounces), cooked and shredded
1 cup frozen corn, thawed
1/3 cup rinsed and drained canned pinto beans
1/3 cup rinsed and drained canned kidney beans
1/2 cup chopped seeded fresh tomato
2 tablespoons drained canned diced mild green chilies
1 green onion, finely chopped
1 teaspoon lime juice
2 ounces reduced-fat Mexican cheese blend or Monterey Jack cheese, cut into 1/3-inch cubes

1. Heat oil in medium nonstick skillet over medium heat until hot. Add garlic. Cook and stir 1 minute. Add red onion, chili powder, cumin and red pepper flakes. Cook and stir 3 minutes. Add chicken, corn and beans. Cook 5 minutes or until heated through, stirring occasionally.

2. Spoon bean mixture into medium serving bowl. Add tomato, chilies, green onion and lime juice; toss to combine. Add cheese; toss to combine. Refrigerate 2 hours before serving.

Makes 2 servings

Nutrients per Serving: 1/2 of total recipe

Calories 336
Fat 10g (sat 4g)
Protein 36g
Carbohydrate 36g
Fiber 6g
Cholesterol 72mg
Sodium 606mg

Exchanges: 2 starch, 1 vegetable, 3 lean meat

Mashed Potatoes and Cauliflower with Sour Cream

Quick Recipe

1-1/4 pounds cauliflower, cut into 1-inch pieces (about 4-1/2 cups)
3/4 pound baking potatoes, peeled and cut into 1/2-inch cubes (about 2-1/2 cups)
1/3 cup reduced-fat sour cream
1 tablespoon minced chives
1/2 teaspoon salt
1/4 teaspoon black pepper

1. Combine cauliflower and potatoes in large saucepan; cover with water. Bring to a boil. Reduce heat; simmer about 10 to 12 minutes or until vegetables are tender. Drain.

2. Add sour cream, chives, salt and pepper to saucepan. Using potato masher, mash until combined.

Makes 6 servings

Nutrients per Serving: 1/2 cup

Calories 83
Fat 2g (sat 1g)
Protein 4g
Carbohydrate 16g
Fiber 3g
Cholesterol 7mg
Sodium 233mg

Exchanges: 1/2 starch, 2 vegetable

Tip

To seed a tomato, first cut it in half crosswise; then hold each half over a bowl, cut side down, and gently squeeze to remove the seeds. Or, simply remove the seeds with a small spoon.

Potatoes au Gratin

(Pictured at right)

1 pound baking potatoes
4 teaspoons reduced-fat butter
4 teaspoons all-purpose flour
1-1/4 cups fat-free milk
1/4 teaspoon ground nutmeg
1/4 teaspoon paprika
    Dash white pepper
1/2 cup thinly sliced red onion
1/3 cup whole wheat bread crumbs
1 tablespoon finely chopped red onion
1 tablespoon grated Parmesan cheese

1. Spray 4- or 6-cup casserole with nonstick cooking spray; set aside.

2. Place potatoes in large saucepan. Add enough water to cover. Bring to a boil over high heat. Boil 12 minutes or until potatoes are tender. Drain; let potatoes stand 10 minutes or until cool enough to handle.

3. Melt butter in small saucepan over medium heat. Add flour. Cook and stir 3 minutes or until small clumps form. Gradually whisk in milk. Cook 8 minutes or until sauce thickens, stirring constantly. Remove saucepan from heat. Stir in nutmeg, paprika and pepper.

4. Preheat oven to 350°F. Cut potatoes into thin slices. Arrange half of potato slices in prepared casserole. Sprinkle with half of onion slices. Repeat layers. Spoon sauce over top. Combine bread crumbs, finely chopped red onion and cheese in small bowl. Sprinkle mixture evenly over sauce. Bake, uncovered, 20 minutes. Let stand 5 minutes before serving.

Makes 4 servings

Nutrients per Serving: about 3/4 cup potatoes

Calories 171	**Fiber** 2g
Fat 3g (sat 2g)	**Cholesterol** 7mg
Protein 6g	**Sodium** 139mg
Carbohydrate 33g	

Exchanges: 2 starch, 1/2 vegetable, 1/2 fat

Sweet Potato Puffs

2 pounds sweet potatoes
1/3 cup orange juice
1 egg, beaten
1 tablespoon grated orange peel
1/2 teaspoon ground nutmeg
1/4 cup chopped pecans

1. Peel and cut sweet potatoes into 1-inch pieces. Place potatoes in medium saucepan. Add enough water to cover. Bring to a boil over medium-high heat. Cook 10 to 15 minutes or until tender.

2. Drain potatoes and place in large bowl; mash until smooth. Add orange juice, egg, orange peel and nutmeg; mix well.

3. Preheat oven to 375°F. Spray baking sheet with nonstick cooking spray. Spoon potato mixture in 10 mounds onto baking sheet. Sprinkle pecans onto tops of mounds. Bake 30 minutes or until centers are hot.

Makes 10 servings

Nutrients per Serving: 1 puff

Calories 103	**Fiber** 2g
Fat 3g (sat <1g)	**Cholesterol** 21mg
Protein 2g	**Sodium** 14mg
Carbohydrate 19g	

Exchanges: 1 starch, 1 vegetable, 1/2 fat

Tip

Baking potatoes and sweet potatoes are similar in weight. Three medium-size potatoes equal about one pound.

Potatoes au Gratin

Taco Salad

Taco Salad

(Pictured above)

3 ounces uncooked radiatore pasta, cooked

1/2 cup frozen corn, thawed

1/2 cup chopped seeded fresh tomato

1 can (4 ounces) diced mild green chilies, drained

1/4 cup chopped onion

2 tablespoons sliced ripe olives

2 tablespoons chopped fresh cilantro

1/2 cup prepared chunky salsa

1/2 teaspoon chili powder

Combine pasta, corn, tomato, chilies, onion, olives and cilantro in large bowl. Combine salsa and chili powder in small bowl until well blended. Pour over pasta mixture. Toss to coat. Cover; refrigerate 2 hours.   *Makes 6 servings*

Nutrients per Serving: 3/4 cup salad

Calories 84	**Fiber** 2g
Fat 2g (sat <1g)	**Cholesterol** 1mg
Protein 3g	**Sodium** 471mg
Carbohydrate 16g	

Exchanges: 1 starch

Pear and Cranberry Salad

Quick Recipe

1/2 cup canned whole-berry cranberry sauce

2 tablespoons balsamic vinegar

1 tablespoon olive oil

12 cups (9 ounces) packed assorted bitter or gourmet salad greens

6 small or 4 large pears (about 1-3/4 pounds)

1/2 cup blue or Gorgonzola cheese, crumbled

Black pepper

1. Combine cranberry sauce, vinegar and oil in small bowl; mix well. (Dressing may be covered and refrigerated up to 2 days before serving.)

2. Arrange greens on 6 serving plates. Cut pears lengthwise into 1/2-inch-thick slices; remove core and seeds from each slice. Arrange pears attractively over greens. Drizzle cranberry dressing over pears and greens; sprinkle with cheese. Sprinkle with pepper to taste.

Makes 6 servings

Note: Be sure to use ripe pears. Forelles and Red Bartletts are particularly well suited for this salad.

Nutrients per Serving: 2 cups greens with 1 small pear, about 1-1/2 tablespoons dressing and 1 tablespoon plus 1 teaspoon blue cheese

Calories 161	**Fiber** 2g
Fat 6g (sat 2g)	**Cholesterol** 7mg
Protein 4g	**Sodium** 165mg
Carbohydrate 26g	

Exchanges: 1 fruit, 2 vegetable, 1/2 lean meat, 1/2 fat

Take-and-Shake Salad

high fiber

Quick Recipe   *(Pictured at right)*

- **1 can (15 ounces) garbanzo beans, rinsed and drained**
- **1 pint cherry tomatoes (preferably sweet grape variety)**
- **1 can (14 ounces) quartered artichoke hearts, drained**
- **1/2 medium green bell pepper, chopped**
- **4 ounces sliced fresh mushrooms**
- **4 ounces crumbled feta cheese *or* 1 cup diced cooked boneless skinless chicken breast**
- **1 can (2-1/4 ounces) sliced ripe olives, drained**
- **2/3 cup cider vinegar**
- **1-1/2 tablespoons olive oil**
- **2 packets sugar substitute***
- **1 teaspoon dried oregano leaves**
- **1/4 teaspoon black pepper**
- **5 cups chopped romaine lettuce**

This recipe was tested with SPLENDA® Packets.

1. Combine beans, tomatoes, artichoke hearts, bell pepper, mushrooms, feta and olives in large mixing bowl. Toss gently to blend. Place equal amounts of salad mixture into 5 large resealable plastic bags.

2. Combine vinegar, oil, sugar substitute, oregano and black pepper in measuring cup. Whisk until well blended. Spoon 3 tablespoons dressing into 5 small resealable plastic bags. Seal and place one in each salad bag. Seal and refrigerate until needed.

3. To transport, add 1 cup of lettuce to each salad bag the day salad is being served. (Do not add lettuce prior to that time or it will become limp.)

4. To serve, pour dressing into large bag with salad. Seal bag and toss to coat salad with dressing.   *Makes 5 servings*

Nutrients per Serving: about 3 cups salad

Calories 262	**Fiber** 9g
Fat 12g (sat 4g)	**Cholesterol** 20mg
Protein 12g	**Sodium** 950mg
Carbohydrate 30g	

Exchanges: 1-1/2 starch, 1-1/2 vegetable, 1 lean meat, 1-1/2 fat

Rice Pilaf with Dried Cherries and Almonds

meatless

Quick Recipe   *(Pictured on page 104)*

- **1/2 cup slivered almonds**
- **2 tablespoons butter**
- **2 cups uncooked converted rice**
- **1/2 cup chopped onion**
- **1 can (14 ounces) vegetable broth**
- **1-1/2 cups water**
- **1/2 cup dried cherries**

1. Cook and stir almonds in large nonstick skillet over medium heat until lightly browned. Remove from skillet; cool.

2. Melt butter in skillet over low heat. Add rice and onion; cook and stir until rice is lightly browned. Add broth and water; bring to a boil over high heat. Reduce heat to low. Simmer, covered, 15 minutes.

3. Stir in almonds and cherries. Simmer 5 minutes or until liquid is absorbed and rice is tender.
              Makes 12 servings

Nutrients per Serving: 1/2 cup pilaf

Calories 189	**Fiber** 1g
Fat 5g (sat 1g)	**Cholesterol** 5mg
Protein 4g	**Sodium** 152mg
Carbohydrate 32g	

Exchanges: 2 starch, 1 fat

Take-and-Shake Salad

Taco Salad

Taco Salad

(Pictured above)

> **3 ounces uncooked radiatore pasta, cooked**
> **1/2 cup frozen corn, thawed**
> **1/2 cup chopped seeded fresh tomato**
> **1 can (4 ounces) diced mild green chilies, drained**
> **1/4 cup chopped onion**
> **2 tablespoons sliced ripe olives**
> **2 tablespoons chopped fresh cilantro**
> **1/2 cup prepared chunky salsa**
> **1/2 teaspoon chili powder**

Combine pasta, corn, tomato, chilies, onion, olives and cilantro in large bowl. Combine salsa and chili powder in small bowl until well blended. Pour over pasta mixture. Toss to coat. Cover; refrigerate 2 hours.   *Makes 6 servings*

Nutrients per Serving: 3/4 cup salad

Calories 84	**Fiber** 2g
Fat 2g (sat <1g)	**Cholesterol** 1mg
Protein 3g	**Sodium** 471mg
Carbohydrate 16g	

Exchanges: 1 starch

Pear and Cranberry Salad

Quick Recipe

> **1/2 cup canned whole-berry cranberry sauce**
> **2 tablespoons balsamic vinegar**
> **1 tablespoon olive oil**
> **12 cups (9 ounces) packed assorted bitter or gourmet salad greens**
> **6 small or 4 large pears (about 1-3/4 pounds)**
> **1/2 cup blue or Gorgonzola cheese, crumbled**
> **Black pepper**

1. Combine cranberry sauce, vinegar and oil in small bowl; mix well. (Dressing may be covered and refrigerated up to 2 days before serving.)

2. Arrange greens on 6 serving plates. Cut pears lengthwise into 1/2-inch-thick slices; remove core and seeds from each slice. Arrange pears attractively over greens. Drizzle cranberry dressing over pears and greens; sprinkle with cheese. Sprinkle with pepper to taste.

Makes 6 servings

Note: Be sure to use ripe pears. Forelles and Red Bartletts are particularly well suited for this salad.

Nutrients per Serving: 2 cups greens with 1 small pear, about 1-1/2 tablespoons dressing and 1 tablespoon plus 1 teaspoon blue cheese

Calories 161	**Fiber** 2g
Fat 6g (sat 2g)	**Cholesterol** 7mg
Protein 4g	**Sodium** 165mg
Carbohydrate 26g	

Exchanges: 1 fruit, 2 vegetable, 1/2 lean meat, 1/2 fat

Mediterranean Veggie Salad

Quick Recipe (Pictured at bottom right)

- **2 ounces (about 2/3 cup) uncooked whole wheat rotini**
- **1/2 cup seeded and diced fresh tomato (about 3 ounces)**
- **1/2 cup thinly sliced zucchini (about 2 ounces)**
- **1/2 cup thin green bell pepper slivers**
- **1/4 cup finely chopped red onion**
- **2 tablespoons coarsely chopped green olives**
- **2 to 3 teaspoons cider vinegar**
- **1 teaspoon dried oregano leaves**
- **1/2 teaspoon dried basil leaves**
- **1/2 medium clove garlic, minced**
- **1 teaspoon extra-virgin olive oil**
- **1/4 teaspoon salt**
- **1/2 cup feta cheese, crumbled**

1. Cook pasta according to package directions, omitting salt. Drain well. Rinse under cold water until completely cooled. Drain.

2. Meanwhile, combine tomatoes, zucchini, bell pepper, onion, olives, vinegar, oregano, basil and garlic in large bowl; toss well.

3. Add cooled pasta, oil and salt to tomato mixture; toss gently to combine. Top with cheese; do not stir. *Makes 5 servings*

Nutrients per Serving: about 1/2 cup salad

Calories 95	**Fiber** 1g
Fat 4g (sat 2g)	**Cholesterol** 10mg
Protein 4g	**Sodium** 314mg
Carbohydrate 12g	

Exchanges: 1/2 starch, 1 vegetable, 1/2 lean meat

Spinach Cheese Pie

- **1 package (10 ounces) frozen chopped spinach, thawed**
- **2 cups reduced-fat Cheddar cheese cubes**
- **1 cup fat-free cottage cheese**
- **1 cup egg substitute**
- **1/2 teaspoon salt**
- **1/4 teaspoon black pepper**
- **3 tablespoons whole wheat flour**

1. Preheat oven to 350°F. Spray 8-inch square baking dish with nonstick cooking spray.

2. Combine all ingredients in large mixing bowl; pour into prepared dish. Bake 1 hour or until set. Cut into 6 squares to serve. *Makes 6 servings*

Nutrients per Serving: 1 pie square

Calories 155	**Fiber** 2g
Fat 4g (sat 2g)	**Cholesterol** 10mg
Protein 21g	**Sodium** 664mg
Carbohydrate 7g	

Exchanges: 1-1/2 vegetable, 2-1/2 lean meat

Mediterranean Veggie Salad

Soups & Sandwiches

ɝɝ ɝɝ ɝɝ

Grilled Salsa Turkey Burger

cooking for 1 or 2

Quick Recipe   *(Pictured at left)*

> 3 ounces 93% lean ground turkey breast
> 1 tablespoon prepared mild or medium salsa
> 1 tablespoon crushed baked tortilla chips
> 1 slice (1 ounce) reduced-fat Monterey Jack cheese
> 1 whole wheat hamburger bun, split
> 1 lettuce leaf
>   Additional salsa (optional)

1. Combine turkey, 1 tablespoon salsa and chips in small bowl; mix lightly. Shape into patty. Lightly spray cold grid of grill or broiler rack with nonstick cooking spray.

2. Grill over medium-hot coals or broil 4 to 6 inches from heat 6 minutes per side or until no longer pink in center, turning once. Top with cheese during last 2 minutes of grilling time, if desired. Place bun, cut sides down, on grill during last 2 minutes of grilling time to toast until lightly browned.

3. Place lettuce on bottom half of bun; top with burger, additional salsa, if desired, and top half of bun.   *Makes 1 serving*

Nutrients per Serving: 1 sandwich

Calories 302	**Fiber** 2g
Fat 11g (sat 3g)	**Cholesterol** 63mg
Protein 22g	**Sodium** 494mg
Carbohydrate 29g	

Exchanges: 2 starch, 2 lean meat, 1 fat

Clockwise from top left: Grilled Salsa Turkey Burger, Indian Carrot Soup (page 134), Thai Chicken Satay (page 130) and Chicken Gumbo (page 138)

Chicken Fajitas with Cowpoke Barbecue Sauce

(Pictured at right)

1 cup Cowpoke Barbecue Sauce (recipe
    follows), divided
10 ounces boneless skinless chicken
    breasts, cut lengthwise into
    1×1/2-inch pieces
2 medium green or red bell peppers,
    cored, seeded and thinly sliced
1 cup sliced onion
2 cups tomato wedges
4 (7-inch) warm flour tortillas

1. Prepare Cowpoke Barbecue Sauce.

2. Spray large nonstick skillet with nonstick cooking spray. Heat over medium-high heat until hot. Brush chicken with 1/4 cup barbecue sauce. Add to skillet. Cook and stir 3 minutes or until chicken is browned.

3. Add peppers and onion to skillet. Cook and stir 3 minutes or until vegetables are crisp-tender and chicken is no longer pink.

4. Add tomatoes to skillet. Cook 2 minutes or until heated through, stirring occasionally.

5. Serve chicken mixture with warm flour tortillas and remaining 3/4 cup Cowpoke Barbecue Sauce. *Makes 4 servings*

Tip

Tortillas can be warmed in an oven, microwave or skillet. To warm tortillas in an oven, first preheat the oven to 350°F. Then, wrap the tortillas in foil and place the foil packet on the oven's center rack. Heat for 10 minutes or until warm.

Cowpoke Barbecue Sauce

1 teaspoon canola oil
3/4 cup chopped green onions
3 cloves garlic, finely chopped
1 can (14-1/2 ounces) crushed tomatoes
1/2 cup ketchup
1/4 cup water
1/4 cup orange juice
2 tablespoons cider vinegar
2 teaspoons chili sauce
    Dash Worcestershire sauce

1. Heat oil in large nonstick saucepan over medium heat until hot. Add onions and garlic. Cook and stir 5 minutes or until onions are tender.

2. Stir in remaining ingredients. Reduce heat to medium-low. Cook 15 minutes, stirring occasionally. *Makes 2 cups*

Nutrients per Serving: 1 fajita with 3 tablespoons barbecue sauce

Calories 266	Fiber 5g
Fat 4g (sat 1g)	Cholesterol 41mg
Protein 22g	Sodium 533mg
Carbohydrate 37g	

Exchanges: 2 starch, 1-1/2 vegetable, 2 lean meat

Chicken Fajita with Cowpoke Barbecue Sauce

Pozole

Quick Recipe   *(Pictured at right)*

1 large onion, thinly sliced
1 tablespoon olive oil
2 teaspoons dried oregano leaves
1/2 teaspoon ground cumin
1 clove garlic, minced
2 cans (14 ounces each) fat-free reduced-sodium chicken broth
1 package (10 ounces) frozen corn
1 to 2 cans (4 ounces each) chopped green chilies, undrained
1 can (2-1/4 ounces) sliced ripe olives, drained
3/4 pound boneless skinless chicken breasts

1. Combine onion, oil, oregano, cumin and garlic in Dutch oven. Cover and cook over medium heat about 6 minutes or until onion is tender, stirring occasionally.

2. Stir broth, corn, chilies and olives into onion mixture. Cover and bring to a boil over high heat.

3. While soup is cooking, cut chicken into thin strips. Add to soup. Reduce heat to medium-low; cover and cook 3 to 4 minutes or until chicken is no longer pink.   *Makes 6 servings*

Note: A Dutch oven is a large pot or kettle with a tight-fitting lid that prevents steam from escaping.

Nutrients per Serving: about 1-1/3 cups Pozole

Calories 142	**Fiber** 3g
Fat 3g (sat <1g)	**Cholesterol** 31mg
Protein 17g	**Sodium** 633mg
Carbohydrate 15g	

Exchanges: 1/2 starch, 1 vegetable, 1-1/2 lean meat, 1 fat

Thai Chicken Satay

(Pictured on page 126)

1 cup plain reduced-fat yogurt
1/2 cup coconut milk
1 tablespoon curry powder
1 teaspoon grated fresh gingerroot
1 teaspoon lemon juice
1/2 teaspoon salt
1/2 teaspoon black pepper
1 clove garlic, crushed
1 pound chicken tenders
6 (6-inch) pita bread rounds, cut in half
Plain reduced-fat yogurt, for garnish (optional)
Chopped fresh cilantro, for garnish (optional)

1. Combine 1 cup yogurt, coconut milk, curry, gingerroot, lemon juice, salt, pepper and garlic in medium bowl; reserve 1/3 cup marinade. Add chicken to remaining marinade; cover and refrigerate at least 8 hours.

2. Soak 12 (10-inch) wooden skewers in water 30 minutes.

3. Remove chicken from marinade; discard marinade. Thread chicken onto skewers. Place skewers on broiler rack coated with nonstick cooking spray; place rack on broiler pan. Broil 4 to 5 inches from heat source 4 to 5 minutes. Turn skewers; brush with reserved 1/3 cup marinade. Discard any remaining marinade. Broil 4 minutes or until chicken is no longer pink in center.

4. Remove chicken from skewers. Fill pitas with chicken and top with dollop of yogurt and cilantro, if desired.   *Makes 6 servings*

Nutrients per Serving: 2 filled pita halves

Calories 327	**Fiber** 2g
Fat 7g (sat 5g)	**Cholesterol** 46mg
Protein 26g	**Sodium** 589mg
Carbohydrate 38g	

Exchanges: 2-1/2 starch, 2 lean meat, 1 fat

Curried Creamy Sweet Potato Soup

pepper, if desired. Cover and blend until completely smooth. Return potato mixture to saucepan and stir in remaining 1 cup milk. Cook 5 minutes over medium-high heat or until heated through. Remove from heat and stir in remaining 1 tablespoon butter.

Makes 4 servings

Nutrients per Serving: 3/4 cup soup

Calories 201	**Fiber** 4g
Fat 5g (sat 3g)	**Cholesterol** 13mg
Protein 7g	**Sodium** 406mg
Carbohydrate 35g	

Exchanges: 1-1/2 starch, 1/2 milk, 1 vegetable, 1 fat

Curried Creamy Sweet Potato Soup

meatless

(Pictured above)

4 cups water
1 pound sweet potatoes, peeled and cut into 1-inch cubes
1 tablespoon plus 1 teaspoon butter, divided
2 cups finely chopped yellow onions
2 cups fat-free milk, divided
3/4 teaspoon curry powder
1/2 teaspoon salt
   Dash ground red pepper (optional)

1. Bring water to a boil in large saucepan over high heat. Add sweet potatoes; return to a boil. Reduce heat to medium-low and simmer, uncovered, 15 minutes or until potatoes are tender.

2. Spray medium nonstick skillet with nonstick cooking spray; heat over medium-high heat until hot. Add 1 teaspoon butter and tilt skillet to coat bottom. Add onions; cook, stirring occasionally, 8 minutes or until tender and golden.

3. Drain potatoes; place in blender with onions, 1 cup milk, curry powder, salt and ground red

Grilled Veggie Burger

low carb
meatless

Quick Recipe

4 frozen meatless veggie burgers (about 2 ounces each)
4 slices sweet onion (such as Vidalia)
4 slices (1 ounce each) reduced-fat Swiss cheese

1. Spray cold grid of grill with nonstick cooking spray. Prepare grill for direct grilling.

2. Grill burgers and onion slices 5 minutes or until burgers are heated through and onion is soft, turning once.

3. Place cheese slices on burgers; top with onion slices. Serve immediately.

Makes 4 servings

Nutrients per Serving: 1 burger with 1 cheese slice and 1 onion slice

Calories 215	**Fiber** 3g
Fat 5g (sat 2g)	**Cholesterol** 15mg
Protein 32g	**Sodium** 410mg
Carbohydrate 8g	

Exchanges: 1-1/2 vegetable, 3-1/2 lean meat

Light Sloppy Joes

Quick Recipe

> 1 small onion, chopped
>
> 1/2 cup diced green or yellow bell pepper
>
> 3 cloves garlic, minced
>
> 1 package JENNIE-O TURKEY STORE® Extra Lean Ground Turkey
>
> 1 can (8 ounces) tomato sauce
>
> 2 tablespoons Worcestershire sauce
>
> 1 tablespoon tomato paste
>
> 3/4 teaspoon salt (optional)
>
> 1/4 teaspoon freshly ground black pepper
>
> 5 kaiser rolls, split, toasted

Coat large nonstick skillet with nonstick cooking spray; place over medium heat. Add onion, bell pepper and garlic; cook 3 minutes, stirring occasionally. Crumble turkey into skillet; cook 3 minutes, stirring occasionally. Add tomato sauce, Worcestershire, tomato paste, salt and pepper. Simmer, uncovered, 10 to 15 minutes or until sauce thickens. Spoon mixture onto rolls.

Makes 5 servings

Nutrients per Serving: 1 roll with 2/3 cup sloppy joe mixture

Calories 225	**Fiber** 3g
Fat 4g (sat 1g)	**Cholesterol** 45mg
Protein 33g	**Sodium** 679mg
Carbohydrate 39g	

Exchanges: 2 starch, 1 vegetable, 3 lean meat

Grilled Portobello Mushroom Sandwich

high fiber · meatless · cooking for 1 or 2

Quick Recipe   *(Pictured at right)*

> 1 large portobello mushroom, cleaned and stemmed
>
> 1 thin slice red onion
>
> 1/4 medium green bell pepper, halved
>
> 1 whole wheat hamburger bun, split
>
> 2 tablespoons prepared fat-free Italian salad dressing
>
> 1 slice (1 ounce) reduced-fat mozzarella cheese

1. Brush mushroom, onion, bell pepper and cut sides of bun with some of dressing; set bun aside. Grill vegetables over medium-hot coals 2 minutes. Turn vegetables over; brush with dressing. Grill 2 minutes more or until tender. Remove onion and bell pepper from grill.

2. Place bun halves, cut sides down, on grill. Arrange mushroom, top side up; brush with any remaining dressing and top with cheese. Grill 1 minute or until cheese is melted and bun is lightly toasted.

3. Cut pepper into strips. Place mushroom on bottom half of bun; top with onion slice and pepper strips. Cover with top half of bun.

Makes 1 serving

Note: To broil, brush mushroom, onion, bell pepper and cut sides of bun with dressing. Place vegetables on greased rack of broiler pan; set bun aside. Broil vegetables 4 to 6 inches from heat 3 minutes; turn over. Brush with dressing. Broil 3 minutes more or until vegetables are tender. Arrange mushroom, top side up, on broiler pan; top with cheese. Place bun halves, cut sides up, on broiler pan. Broil both 1 minute or until cheese is melted and bun is toasted. Assemble sandwich as directed above.

Nutrients per Serving: 1 sandwich

Calories 225	**Fiber** 6g
Fat 6g (sat 3g)	**Cholesterol** 27mg
Protein 15g	**Sodium** 729mg
Carbohydrate 30g	

Exchanges: 2 starch, 1 lean meat, 1/2 fat

Grilled Portobello Mushroom Sandwich

Pulled Pork Barbecue

(Pictured at right)

1 whole pork tenderloin (about 1 pound),
all fat trimmed
1 teaspoon chili powder
1/2 teaspoon garlic powder
Vegetable cooking spray
1/2 cup finely chopped onion
1-1/2 teaspoons minced garlic
1 can (15 ounces) crushed tomatoes,
undrained
1 tablespoon cider vinegar
1 tablespoon prepared mustard
1 to 2 teaspoons chili powder
1/4 teaspoon maple extract
1/4 teaspoon liquid smoke
1/3 cup EQUAL® SPOONFUL*
Salt and pepper
6 multigrain hamburger buns, toasted

*May substitute 8 packets EQUAL® sweetener.

• Rub pork with 1 teaspoon chili powder and garlic powder; place in baking pan. Bake in preheated 425°F oven until pork is well browned and juices run clear, 30 to 40 minutes. Let stand 10 to 15 minutes. Cut into 2- to 3-inch slices; shred slices into bite-size pieces with fork.

• Spray medium saucepan with cooking spray; heat over medium heat until hot. Sauté onion and garlic until tender, about 5 minutes. Add tomatoes, vinegar, mustard, chili powder, maple extract and liquid smoke to saucepan; heat to boiling. Reduce heat and simmer, uncovered, until medium sauce consistency, 10 to 15 minutes. Stir in Equal®. Season to taste with salt and pepper. Stir pork into sauce; cook until hot, 2 to 3 minutes. Spoon mixture into buns.

Makes 6 servings

Nutrients per Serving: 1 bun with 1/2 cup pork mixture (without salt and pepper seasoning)

Calories 234	**Fiber** 3g
Fat 5g (sat 1g)	**Cholesterol** 45mg
Protein 20g	**Sodium** 436mg
Carbohydrate 27g	

Exchanges: 2 starch, 2 lean meat

Indian Carrot Soup

(Pictured on page 126)

1 small onion, chopped
1 tablespoon minced fresh gingerroot
1 teaspoon olive oil
1-1/2 teaspoons curry powder
1/2 teaspoon ground cumin
2 cans (14 ounces each) fat-free reduced-
sodium chicken broth, divided
1 pound peeled baby carrots
1 tablespoon sugar
1/4 teaspoon ground cinnamon
Dash ground red pepper
2 teaspoons fresh lime juice
3 tablespoons chopped fresh cilantro
1/4 cup plain fat-free yogurt

1. Spray large saucepan with nonstick cooking spray; heat over medium heat. Add onion and gingerroot; reduce heat to low. Cover; cook 3 to 4 minutes or until onion is transparent and crisp-tender, stirring occasionally. Add olive oil; cook and stir, uncovered, 3 to 4 minutes or until onion just turns golden. Add curry powder and cumin; cook and stir 30 seconds or until fragrant. Add 1 can chicken broth and carrots; bring to a boil over high heat. Reduce heat to low; simmer, covered, 15 minutes or until carrots are tender. Cool slightly.

2. Ladle carrot mixture into food processor; cover and process until smooth. Return to saucepan; stir in remaining 1 can chicken broth, sugar, cinnamon and red pepper. Bring to a boil over medium heat. Remove from heat; stir in lime juice. Ladle into bowls; sprinkle with cilantro. Top each serving with 1 tablespoon yogurt.

Makes 4 servings

Nutrients per Serving: about 1 cup soup

Calories 99	**Fiber** 1g
Fat 2g (sat <1g)	**Cholesterol** <1mg
Protein 3g	**Sodium** 77mg
Carbohydrate 17g	

Exchanges: 1/2 starch, 2 vegetable

Pulled Pork Barbecue

Southwestern Beef Stew

(Pictured at right)

1/4 cup all-purpose flour
1 teaspoon salt
1 teaspoon chili powder
1 teaspoon ground cumin
1 pound beef stew meat, trimmed of fat
and cut into 1-inch cubes
2 teaspoons canola oil
1 large onion, cut into chunks
2 teaspoons minced garlic
1 can (14 ounces) fat-free
reduced-sodium beef broth
1/2 cup prepared salsa or picante sauce
3/4 pound red potatoes, cut into 1-inch
chunks
2 medium green or yellow bell peppers
(or 1 of each), cut into 1-inch chunks
1 cup baby carrots (about 4 ounces)
1/4 cup chopped fresh cilantro

1. Combine flour and seasonings in small bowl.
Reserve 1 tablespoon mixture. Place remaining
mixture in large resealable plastic bag. Add beef;
shake to coat. Heat oil in large deep nonstick
skillet or Dutch oven over medium heat until
hot. Transfer beef to skillet. Discard bag. Brown
beef on all sides, about 5 minutes. Remove from
skillet; set aside.

2. Add onion and garlic to same skillet.
Cook 5 minutes over medium heat, stirring
occasionally. Sprinkle reserved 1 tablespoon
flour mixture over mixture in skillet; cook and
stir 1 minute. Add beef broth and salsa; bring to
a boil. Return beef and any accumulated juices
to skillet. Reduce heat; cover and simmer over
low heat 40 minutes.

3. Stir in potatoes, bell peppers and carrots.
Cover; simmer 35 to 40 minutes or until beef
and vegetables are tender. Sprinkle with cilantro.

Makes 6 servings

Serving Suggestion: Cornbread is the perfect
accompaniment to this flavorful stew.

Nutrients per Serving: 1-1/4 cups stew

Calories 225	**Fiber** 3g
Fat 6g (sat 2g)	**Cholesterol** 47mg
Protein 24g	**Sodium** 622mg
Carbohydrate 20g	

Exchanges: 1 starch, 1 vegetable, 2 lean meat

❧ ❧ ❧

Mediterranean Tuna Sandwich

high fiber

Quick Recipe

1 can (12 ounces) solid white tuna packed
in water, drained and flaked
1/4 cup finely chopped red onion
1/4 cup fat-free mayonnaise
3 tablespoons chopped drained canned
ripe olives
1 tablespoon chopped fresh mint
1 tablespoon plus 1 teaspoon lemon juice
1 tablespoon olive oil
1/4 teaspoon black pepper
1/8 teaspoon garlic powder
8 slices whole wheat bread
4 thin fresh tomato slices

1. Combine tuna, onion, mayonnaise, olives,
mint, lemon juice, olive oil, pepper and garlic
powder in large bowl.

2. Top each of 4 bread slices with 1 tomato
slice. Spoon 2/3 cup tuna mixture over each
tomato slice. Top with remaining bread slices.
Cut sandwiches in half to serve.

Makes 4 servings

Nutrients per Serving: 1 sandwich (2 halves)

Calories 301	**Fiber** 5g
Fat 7g (sat 1g)	**Cholesterol** 54mg
Protein 28g	**Sodium** 817mg
Carbohydrate 31g	

Exchanges: 2 starch, 1/2 vegetable, 2-1/2 lean meat

Southwestern Beef Stew

Chicken Gumbo

(Pictured on page 126)

2 tablespoons all-purpose flour
2 teaspoons blackened seasoning mix or Creole seasoning mix
3/4 pound boneless skinless chicken thighs, cut into 3/4-inch pieces
2 teaspoons olive oil
1 large onion, coarsely chopped
1/2 cup sliced celery
2 teaspoons minced garlic
1 can (14-1/2 ounces) stewed tomatoes
1 can (14 ounces) fat-free reduced-sodium chicken broth
1 large green bell pepper, cut into pieces
1 teaspoon filé powder (optional)
2 cups hot cooked rice
2 tablespoons chopped fresh parsley

1. Combine flour and blackened seasoning mix in large resealable plastic bag. Add chicken; toss to coat. Heat oil in large deep nonstick skillet or saucepan over medium heat. Add chicken to skillet; sprinkle with any remaining flour mixture. Cook and stir 3 minutes. Add onion, celery and garlic; cook and stir 3 minutes.

2. Add tomatoes, chicken broth and bell pepper; bring to a boil. Reduce heat; cover and simmer 20 minutes or until vegetables are tender. Uncover; simmer 5 to 10 minutes or until sauce is slightly reduced. Remove from heat; stir in filé powder, if desired. Ladle into shallow bowls; top with rice and parsley. *Makes 4 servings*

Note: Filé powder, made from dried sassafras leaves, thickens and adds flavor to gumbos. Look for it in the herb and spice section of your supermarket.

Nutrients per Serving: 1-1/2 cups gumbo with 1/2 cup rice

Calories 306	**Fiber** 3g
Fat 9g (sat 2g)	**Cholesterol** 46mg
Protein 18g	**Sodium** 212mg
Carbohydrate 38g	

Exchanges: 2 starch, 1-1/2 vegetable, 2 lean meat, 1/2 fat

Light Tex-Mex Chili

low fat | high fiber

Quick Recipe

Cooking spray
1 medium onion, chopped
3 cloves garlic, minced
1 package JENNIE-O TURKEY STORE® Extra Lean Ground Turkey Breast
1 tablespoon chili powder
1 tablespoon ground cumin
3/4 teaspoon salt (optional)
2 cans (14-1/2 ounces each) salsa-style or regular stewed tomatoes, undrained
1 can (15 ounces) kidney or pinto beans, rinsed and drained
1 green bell pepper, diced
3/4 cup picante sauce or salsa
Optional toppings: shredded low-fat Cheddar cheese, nonfat or light sour cream, chopped cilantro

Coat large saucepan with cooking spray. Add onion and garlic; cook over medium heat 5 minutes, stirring occasionally. Crumble turkey into saucepan; sprinkle with chili powder, cumin and salt. Cook 5 minutes, stirring occasionally. Add tomatoes, beans, bell pepper and picante sauce. Bring to a boil over high heat. Reduce heat; simmer uncovered 10 minutes, stirring occasionally. Serve with desired toppings.

Makes 6 servings

Nutrients per Serving: 1-1/3 cups chili (without toppings)

Calories 237	**Fiber** 9g
Fat 2g (sat 1g)	**Cholesterol** 38mg
Protein 28g	**Sodium** 894mg
Carbohydrate 26g	

Exchanges: 1 starch, 2 vegetable, 3 lean meat

Chilled Roasted Red Pepper Soup

low fat • low carb • meatless

- 3 large red bell peppers
- 3 cups vegetable broth
- 1 cup diced onion
- 1 cup water
- 1 tablespoon chopped garlic
- 1 bay leaf
- 1/2 teaspoon celery seeds
- 1/2 teaspoon black pepper
- 2 dashes hot pepper sauce
- Plain fat-free yogurt, for garnish (optional)

1. Preheat oven to 400°F. Place peppers on baking sheet; roast about 30 minutes, turning every 10 minutes, or until charred. Remove peppers from oven; place in bowl and cover with plastic wrap. Set aside 15 minutes.

2. Gently peel charred skin from peppers; discard skin. Cut peppers into quarters. Remove seeds and ribs; discard.

3. Place roasted peppers and all remaining ingredients in medium saucepan. Cover and cook over medium heat 45 minutes. Uncover and let soup cool about 15 minutes. Remove bay leaf; discard. Transfer soup to food processor or blender; cover and process until smooth.

4. Chill soup in refrigerator 3 hours or overnight before serving. Serve with dollop of yogurt, if desired. *Makes 6 servings*

Nutrients per Serving: 3/4 cup soup

Calories 52	**Fiber** 2g
Fat 1g (sat <1g)	**Cholesterol** 0mg
Protein 2g	**Sodium** 505mg
Carbohydrate 10g	

Exchanges: 2 vegetable

Asian Noodle Soup

Quick Recipe (Pictured below)

- 4 ounces uncooked dried Chinese egg noodles
- 3 cans (14 ounces each) fat-free reduced-sodium chicken broth
- 2 slices fresh gingerroot
- 2 cloves garlic, peeled and cut into halves
- 1/2 cup fresh snow peas, cut into 1-inch pieces
- 3 tablespoons chopped green onions
- 1 tablespoon chopped fresh cilantro
- 1-1/2 teaspoons hot chili oil
- 1/2 teaspoon dark sesame oil

1. Cook noodles according to package directions, omitting salt. Drain and set aside.

2. Combine chicken broth, gingerroot and garlic in large saucepan; bring to a boil over high heat. Reduce heat to low; simmer about 15 minutes. Remove gingerroot and garlic with slotted spoon; discard.

3. Add snow peas, green onions, cilantro, chili oil and sesame oil to broth; simmer 3 to 5 minutes. Stir in noodles; serve immediately. *Makes 4 servings*

Nutrients per Serving: about 2 cups soup

Calories 118	**Fiber** 3g
Fat 4g (sat <1g)	**Cholesterol** 4mg
Protein 4g	**Sodium** 152mg
Carbohydrate 17g	

Exchanges: 1/2 starch, 1-1/2 vegetable, 1 fat

Asian Noodle Soup

Turkey Burgers

Quick Recipe   (Pictured at bottom right)

> 1/4 cup Cowpoke Barbecue Sauce
>   (page 128)*
> 1 pound 93% lean ground turkey breast
> 1 cup whole wheat bread crumbs
> 1 egg white
> 1/2 teaspoon dried sage leaves
> 1/2 teaspoon dried marjoram leaves
> 1/4 teaspoon salt
> 1/4 teaspoon black pepper
> 1 teaspoon canola oil
> 4 lettuce leaves
> 4 fresh tomato slices
> 4 whole-grain sandwich rolls, split in half

*Or, substitute prepared barbecue sauce.

1. Prepare Cowpoke Barbecue Sauce. Combine turkey, bread crumbs, egg white, sage, marjoram, salt and pepper in large bowl until well blended. Shape into 4 patties.

2. Heat oil in large nonstick skillet over medium-high heat until hot. Add patties. Cook 10 minutes or until patties are no longer pink in center, turning once.

3. Place lettuce leaf, tomato slice, burger and 1 tablespoon barbecue sauce on each roll.
Makes 4 servings

Nutrients per Serving: 1 sandwich

Calories 319	**Fiber** 2g
Fat 6g (sat 1g)	**Cholesterol** 41mg
Protein 26g	**Sodium** 669mg
Carbohydrate 40g	

Exchanges: 2-1/2 starch, 1/2 vegetable, 3 lean meat

Minute Minestrone Soup

high fiber

Quick Recipe

> 1/2 pound turkey sausage, cut into small
>   pieces
> 2 cloves garlic, crushed
> 3 cans (14-1/2 ounces each) low-sodium
>   chicken broth
> 2 cups frozen Italian blend vegetables
> 1 can (15 ounces) white kidney beans,
>   rinsed and drained
> 1 can (14-1/2 ounces) Italian stewed
>   tomatoes, undrained
> 1 cup cooked ditalini or small shell pasta
>   (1/2 cup uncooked)
> 3 tablespoons *French's®* Worcestershire
>   Sauce

1. In medium saucepan, stir-fry sausage and garlic 5 minutes or until sausage is cooked; drain. Add broth, vegetables, beans and tomatoes. Heat to boiling. Simmer, uncovered, 5 minutes or until vegetables are crisp-tender.

2. Stir in pasta and Worcestershire. Cook until heated through. Serve with grated cheese and crusty bread, if desired.   *Makes 6 servings*

Nutrients per Serving: 1-3/4 cups soup (without cheese and bread)

Calories 231	**Fiber** 6g
Fat 6g (sat 1g)	**Cholesterol** 33mg
Protein 19g	**Sodium** 903mg
Carbohydrate 25g	

Exchanges: 1-1/2 starch, 1 vegetable, 1-1/2 lean meat

Turkey Burger

Shredded Beef Fajita

Shredded Beef Fajitas

(Pictured above)

1 beef flank steak (about 1 pound)
1 medium onion, thinly sliced
1/2 medium green bell pepper, cut into
**   thin strips**
1 clove garlic, minced *or* 1/4 teaspoon
**   garlic powder**
1/2 (1.3-ounce) package fajita seasoning mix
1 can (10 ounces) diced tomatoes with
**   green chilies**
6 (7-inch) flour tortillas
**   Toppings: reduced-fat sour cream,**
**   guacamole, shredded reduced-fat**
**   Cheddar cheese, salsa (optional)**

Slow Cooker Directions

1. Cut flank steak into 6 portions. Combine beef, onion, bell pepper, garlic and fajita seasoning mix in 3-1/2-quart slow cooker. Add tomatoes. Cover; cook on LOW 8 to 10 hours or on HIGH 4 to 5 hours.

2. Remove beef from slow cooker; shred. Return to slow cooker and stir. To serve, divide meat mixture evenly among flour tortillas. Add toppings as desired. Roll up tortillas.

Makes 6 servings

Nutrients per Serving: 1 fajita (without toppings)

Calories 294	**Fiber** 2g
Fat 8g (sat 2g)	**Cholesterol** 25mg
Protein 21g	**Sodium** 863mg
Carbohydrate 33g	

Exchanges: 2 starch, 1/2 vegetable, 2 lean meat

Ham and Broccoli Chowder

Quick Recipe

>   2 cups broccoli florets
>   1 cup chopped onion
>   2 ribs celery, sliced
> 1/4 cup water
>   3 cups fat-free milk
> 1/2 cup all-purpose flour
>   1 teaspoon salt-free Italian seasoning
> 1/4 teaspoon black pepper
>   3 ounces 97% lean ham
> 1/2 cup shredded reduced-fat sharp
>   Cheddar cheese
>   5 green onions, chopped

Microwave Directions

1. Combine broccoli, onion, celery and water in 2-quart microwavable container. Cover and microwave at HIGH 6 minutes, stirring halfway through cooking.

2. Whisk together milk, flour, Italian seasoning and pepper in medium bowl. Stir into vegetables. Cover and microwave at HIGH 6 minutes or until mixture thickens and comes to a boil, stirring every 2 minutes.

3. Cut ham into 1/2-inch pieces. Add ham to broccoli mixture. Cover and microwave at HIGH 1 minute. Add cheese. Cover and let stand 5 minutes. Stir until cheese is melted. To serve, ladle into bowls and sprinkle with green onions.   *Makes 4 servings*

Note: This recipe was tested in an 1100-watt microwave oven.

Nutrients per Serving: 1-1/2 cups chowder

Calories 220	**Fiber** 3g
Fat 4g (sat 2g)	**Cholesterol** 17mg
Protein 18g	**Sodium** 559mg
Carbohydrate 29g	

Exchanges: 1 starch, 1/2 milk, 1-1/2 vegetable, 1 lean meat

Mediterranean Shrimp Soup

>   2 cans (14 ounces each) fat-free reduced-sodium chicken broth
>   1 can (14-1/2 ounces) diced tomatoes
>   1 can (8 ounces) tomato sauce
>   1 medium onion, chopped
> 1/2 medium green bell pepper, chopped
> 1/2 cup orange juice
> 1/2 cup additional fat-free reduced-sodium chicken broth (optional)
>   1 jar (2-1/2 ounces) sliced mushrooms
> 1/4 cup sliced ripe olives
>   2 cloves garlic, minced
>   1 teaspoon dried basil leaves
>   2 bay leaves
> 1/4 teaspoon fennel seeds, crushed
> 1/8 teaspoon black pepper
>   1 pound uncooked medium shrimp, peeled and deveined

Slow Cooker Directions

Place all ingredients except shrimp in 3-1/2-quart slow cooker. Cover; cook on LOW 4 to 4-1/2 hours or until vegetables are crisp-tender. Stir in shrimp. Cover; cook 15 to 30 minutes longer or until shrimp are opaque. Remove bay leaves; discard.

Makes 6 servings

Note: For a heartier soup, add some fish. Cut 1 pound of whitefish or cod into 1-inch pieces. Add the fish to the slow cooker 45 minutes before the end of cooking. Cover and cook on LOW.

Nutrients per Serving: 1-2/3 cups soup (without added fish)

Calories 162	**Fiber** 2g
Fat 3g (sat <1g)	**Cholesterol** 129mg
Protein 21g	**Sodium** 678mg
Carbohydrate 12g	

Exchanges: 2 vegetable, 2 lean meat

Farmer's Market Grilled Chowder

Farmer's Market Grilled Chowder

(Pictured above)

1 ear fresh corn *or* 1 cup frozen corn,
    thawed
Nonstick cooking spray
1 large potato
1 small zucchini, cut lengthwise into
    1/4-inch-thick slices
1 tablespoon butter
1/2 cup chopped onion
2 tablespoons all-purpose flour
1/2 teaspoon salt
1/2 teaspoon dried thyme leaves
1/8 teaspoon white pepper
1 cup fat-free reduced-sodium chicken
    broth
1 cup 1% milk
1/2 cup shredded reduced-fat sharp
    Cheddar cheese

1. Remove husks and silk from corn. Place corn in large bowl and cover with cold water; soak 20 to 30 minutes. Remove from water; wrap in foil. Spray cold grid of grill with cooking spray. Prepare grill for direct grilling. Grill corn on covered grill over medium-hot coals 20 to 25 minutes or until hot and tender, turning over halfway through grilling time. Remove kernels from cob. Set aside.

2. Cut potato in half lengthwise; grill potato halves on covered grill over medium coals 15 to 20 minutes or until potato is tender, turning over once. Remove potato from grill. Cut into cubes.

3. To grill zucchini, spray both sides of zucchini with cooking spray. Grill on uncovered grill over medium coals 4 minutes or until grill-marked and tender, turning once. Remove zucchini from grill. Cool; cut into bite-size pieces. Set aside.

4. Melt butter in large saucepan over medium heat. Add onion; cook and stir 5 minutes or until tender but not brown. Stir in flour, salt, thyme and pepper. Cook and stir about 1 minute.

5. Stir broth and milk into flour mixture. Cook and stir over medium heat until mixture begins to bubble; continue cooking about 1 minute more. Stir in corn, potato, zucchini and cheese. Reduce heat to low; simmer, uncovered, until cheese is melted and mixture is hot, stirring constantly. *Makes 5 servings*

Nutrients per Serving: 1 cup chowder

Calories 174	**Fiber** 2g
Fat 5g (sat 2g)	**Cholesterol** 8mg
Protein 7g	**Sodium** 438mg
Carbohydrate 26g	

Exchanges: 1-1/2 starch, 1/2 vegetable, 1/2 lean meat, 1/2 fat

Tip

Spray the grill grid with cooking spray before you start grilling. This will keep food from sticking to the grid and will make cleanup a lot easier. To prevent flare-ups, never spray the grid over an open fire.

Chili, Vegetarian Style

Quick Recipe

  1 tablespoon extra-virgin olive oil
1-1/3 cups red and yellow bell peppers, chopped
  1/2 cup onion, chopped
  1 jalapeño pepper, seeds removed, finely chopped
  6 teaspoons chili powder
1-1/2 teaspoons paprika
  3/4 teaspoon ground (cayenne) red pepper
  1/4 teaspoon garlic powder
  1/2 cup SPLENDA® No Calorie Sweetener, Granular
  3 tablespoons balsamic vinegar
  1 (28-ounce) can crushed tomatoes with thick tomato purée
  1 (19-ounce) can black beans, undrained
  2 (19-ounce) cans dark red kidney beans, undrained
  1 (19-ounce) can cannellini beans, undrained
  1 (10-ounce) box frozen corn kernels

In large, nonstick stock pot, heat olive oil. Sauté red and yellow peppers, onion and jalapeño pepper over medium heat until onion is translucent, about 5 to 8 minutes. Add remaining ingredients and slowly bring to boil. Cover pot and simmer on low heat 20 minutes. Serve hot. *Serves 16*

Serving Suggestion: Chili tastes best when it is allowed to sit overnight. Refrigerate it in a covered pot overnight. To reheat, bring it to a boil over low heat, stirring constantly.

Note: If hot chili is preferred, increase the ground (cayenne) red pepper to 1 teaspoon and increase the chili powder to 7 teaspoons. If sweeter chili is preferred, increase SPLENDA® to 2/3 cup.

Nutrients per Serving: about 3/4 cup chili

Calories 161
Fat 2g (sat <1g)
Protein 8g
Carbohydrate 29g
Fiber 9g
Cholesterol 0mg
Sodium 546mg

Exchanges: 2 starch, 1/2 lean meat

᠎ ᠎ ᠎

Light Comforting Double Corn Chowder

Quick Recipe

  1 package JENNIE-O TURKEY STORE® Lean Turkey Bratwurst
  1 cup chopped onion
  1 tablespoon all-purpose flour
  2 cups skim milk
  1 can (15 ounces) cream-style corn
  1 cup fresh or frozen corn kernels
  1/2 cup finely diced red or green bell pepper
  1/4 teaspoon freshly ground black pepper
  1/4 teaspoon hot pepper sauce
  1/2 cup seasoned croutons (optional)
  Chopped chives or green onion tops (optional)

Crumble bratwurst into large saucepan; discard casings. Add onion; cook over medium heat 8 minutes, breaking up bratwurst into chunks. Sprinkle with flour; cook 1 minute, stirring constantly. Add milk, creamed corn, corn kernels, bell pepper, black pepper and hot pepper sauce. Simmer, uncovered, 15 minutes, stirring occasionally. Ladle into bowls; top with croutons and chives, if desired.

Makes 6 servings

Nutrients per Serving: about 1-1/3 cups chowder (without toppings)

Calories 262
Fat 9g (sat 2g)
Protein 19g
Carbohydrate 28g
Fiber 2g
Cholesterol 47mg
Sodium 801mg

Exchanges: 1-1/2 starch, 1/2 milk, 2 lean meat

Maui Chicken Sandwich

high fiber

(Pictured at right)

1 can (8 ounces) DOLE® Pineapple Slices

1/2 teaspoon dried oregano leaves, crushed

1/4 teaspoon garlic powder

4 skinless, boneless, small chicken breast halves

1/2 cup light prepared Thousand Island salad dressing

1/2 cup finely chopped jicama or water chestnuts

1/4 teaspoon ground red pepper (optional)

4 whole grain or whole wheat sandwich rolls

DOLE® Red or Green Bell Pepper, sliced into rings, or shredded DOLE® Iceberg Lettuce

• Combine undrained pineapple slices, oregano and garlic powder in shallow, non-metallic dish. Add chicken; turn to coat all sides. Cover and marinate 15 minutes in refrigerator.

• Grill or broil chicken and pineapple, brushing occasionally with marinade, 5 to 8 minutes on each side or until chicken is no longer pink in center and pineapple is golden brown. Do not baste during last 5 minutes of grilling. Discard any remaining marinade.

• Combine dressing, jicama and ground red pepper. Spread on rolls. Top with chicken, bell pepper rings and pineapple. Serve open-face, if desired. *Makes 4 servings*

Nutrients per Serving: 1 sandwich (with whole roll)

Calories 347	**Fiber** 5g
Fat 9g (sat 1g)	**Cholesterol** 87mg
Protein 30g	**Sodium** 608mg
Carbohydrate 38g	

Exchanges: 2 starch, 1/2 fruit, 3 lean meat

Fresh Tomato Pasta Soup

1 tablespoon olive oil

1/2 cup chopped onion

1 clove garlic, minced

3 pounds fresh tomatoes (about 9 medium), coarsely chopped

3 cups fat-free reduced-sodium chicken broth

1 tablespoon minced fresh basil

1 tablespoon minced fresh marjoram

1 tablespoon minced fresh oregano

1 teaspoon fennel seeds

1/2 teaspoon black pepper

3/4 cup uncooked small pasta

1/2 cup shredded part-skim mozzarella cheese

1. Heat oil in large saucepan over medium heat. Add onion and garlic; cook and stir until onion is tender.

2. Add tomatoes, broth, basil, marjoram, oregano, fennel seeds and pepper; bring to a boil. Reduce heat. Cover; simmer 25 minutes. Remove from heat; cool slightly.

3. Transfer tomato mixture to food processor or blender in batches. Cover and purée until smooth. Return to saucepan; bring to a boil. Add pasta; cook 7 to 9 minutes or until pasta is tender. Transfer to serving bowls. Sprinkle with mozzarella. *Makes 8 servings*

Nutrients per Serving: 3/4 cup soup with 1 tablespoon cheese

Calories 130	**Fiber** 3g
Fat 4g (sat 1g)	**Cholesterol** 5mg
Protein 8g	**Sodium** 200mg
Carbohydrate 18g	

Exchanges: 1/2 starch, 2 vegetable, 1/2 fat

Maui Chicken Sandwich

Middle Eastern Lentil Soup

high fiber / meatless

(Pictured at right)

2 tablespoons olive oil

1 medium red bell pepper, chopped

1 small onion, chopped

1 teaspoon fennel seeds

1/2 teaspoon ground cumin

1/4 teaspoon ground red pepper

4 cups water

1 cup dried lentils, sorted and rinsed

1/2 teaspoon salt

1 tablespoon lemon juice

1/2 cup plain reduced-fat yogurt

2 tablespoons chopped fresh parsley

1. Heat oil in large saucepan over medium-high heat until hot. Add bell pepper and onion; cook and stir 5 minutes or until tender. Add fennel seeds, cumin and ground red pepper; cook and stir 1 minute.

2. Add water, lentils and salt. Bring to a boil. Reduce heat to low. Cover and simmer 25 to 30 minutes or until lentils are tender. Stir in lemon juice.

3. To serve, ladle soup into individual bowls and top with yogurt; sprinkle with parsley.

Makes 4 servings

Hint: For a decorative touch, top each serving with yellow bell pepper strips.

Nutrients per Serving: 1 cup soup with 2 tablespoons yogurt and 1-1/2 teaspoons parsley

Calories 266	**Fiber** 16g
Fat 8g (sat 1g)	**Cholesterol** 2mg
Protein 16g	**Sodium** 320mg
Carbohydrate 35g	

Exchanges: 2 starch, 1 vegetable, 1 lean meat, 1 fat

Creamy Dijon Turkey Soup

Quick Recipe

1 cup each chopped celery and thinly sliced onions

3 tablespoons margarine

1 large clove garlic, minced

3 tablespoons all-purpose flour

1/2 teaspoon salt

1/4 teaspoon white pepper

4 cups skim milk

1/4 cup Dijon mustard

2 teaspoons reduced-sodium chicken bouillon granules

2 cups cubed cooked turkey (1/2- to 3/4-inch cubes)

French bread (optional)

1. In 3-quart saucepan, over medium-high heat, sauté celery and onions in margarine 5 to 6 minutes or until celery is tender and onions are golden-brown. Add garlic and sauté 1 minute. Stir in flour, salt and pepper and cook 1 to 2 minutes. Remove pan from heat and slowly add milk, stirring constantly.

2. Return pan to medium-high heat. Stir in mustard and bouillon; cook and stir 5 to 8 minutes or until mixture is thickened and bubbly. Stir in turkey and heat 1 to 2 minutes. Serve with sliced French bread, if desired.

Makes 6 servings

Favorite recipe from **National Turkey Federation**

Nutrients per Serving: about 1-1/3 cups soup

Calories 233	**Fiber** 1g
Fat 9g (sat 2g)	**Cholesterol** 39mg
Protein 21g	**Sodium** 689mg
Carbohydrate 17g	

Exchanges: 1/2 starch, 1/2 milk, 1/2 vegetable, 2-1/2 lean meat

Middle Eastern Lentil Soup

Desserts

৯ঌ ৯ঌ ৯ঌ

Peaches & Cream Gingersnap Cups

cooking for 1 or 2

(Pictured at left)

1-1/2 tablespoons gingersnap crumbs (2 cookies)
1/4 teaspoon ground ginger
2 ounces reduced-fat cream cheese, softened
1 container (6 ounces) peach sugar-free fat-free yogurt
1/4 teaspoon vanilla extract
1/3 cup chopped fresh peach or drained canned peach slices in juice

1. Combine gingersnap crumbs and ginger in small bowl; set aside.

2. Beat cream cheese in small bowl at medium speed of electric mixer until smooth. Add yogurt and vanilla. Beat at low speed until smooth and well blended. Stir in chopped peach.

3. Divide peach mixture between 2 (6-ounce) custard cups. Cover and refrigerate 1 hour. Top each serving with half of reserved gingersnap crumbs just before serving.   *Makes 2 servings*

Nutrients per Serving: 1 dessert cup (1/2 of total recipe)

Calories 148   **Fiber** 1g
Fat 5g (sat 3g)   **Cholesterol** 16mg
Protein 6g   **Sodium** 204mg
Carbohydrate 18g

Exchanges: 1 starch, 1/2 milk, 1/2 fat

***Clockwise from top left:** Lemon Meringue Pie (page 169), Peaches & Cream Gingersnap Cups, Chocolate-Strawberry Crêpes (page 166) and Chocolate Orange Cake Roll (page 163)*

Cocoa-Cherry Chill

(Pictured at right)

**1 can (14-1/2 ounces) tart cherries
packed in water, undrained**
**1-1/2 cups frozen unsweetened pitted Bing
cherries**
1 cup fat-free half-and-half
1/2 cup reduced-fat chocolate syrup
1 teaspoon vanilla extract

1. Place tart cherries with can liquid, frozen Bing cherries, half-and-half and chocolate syrup in blender. Cover and process at high speed until very smooth.

2. Add vanilla extract to blender container. Cover and blend until smooth, scraping sides occasionally to mix well. Freeze mixture in ice cream maker according to manufacturer's instructions.

3. Remove from freezer and scoop into serving dishes. For best flavor, let stand 15 minutes at room temperature before serving. Garnish as desired. *Makes 8 servings*

Nutrients per Serving: 1/2 cup

Calories 62	**Fiber** 1g
Fat <1g (sat <1g)	**Cholesterol** 4mg
Protein 2g	**Sodium** 41mg
Carbohydrate 14g	

Exchanges: 1/2 starch, 1/2 fruit

Lemon Almond Biscotti

1/3 cup butter, softened
2/3 cup sugar
2 tablespoons grated lemon peel
1 teaspoon baking powder
1/2 teaspoon baking soda
1/8 teaspoon salt
2 large eggs
2-1/2 cups all-purpose flour
1/2 cup slivered almonds

1. Preheat oven to 375°F. Beat butter in large bowl with electric mixer at medium speed 30 seconds. Add sugar, lemon peel, baking powder, baking soda and salt. Beat until well blended. Beat in eggs. Beat in flour to crumb texture. (It will be fairly dry at this point.) Stir in almonds.

2. Kneading dough slightly, shape into 2 (9-inch) logs. Flatten logs with palm of hand to 1-1/2-inch thickness. Place on nonstick baking sheet. Bake 20 minutes or until wooden toothpick inserted into centers of rolls comes out clean. Remove from oven and let cool on baking sheet 1 hour.

3. Slice each roll crosswise into 16 (1/2-inch) slices.

4. Place slices, cut side down, on baking sheet; bake 8 minutes. Turn and bake 8 minutes more or until crisp and golden. Remove to wire rack; cool. Store up to 3 days in airtight container. *Makes 32 servings*

Nutrients per Serving: 1 biscotti

Calories 85	**Fiber** <1g
Fat 3g (sat 1g)	**Cholesterol** 18mg
Protein 2g	**Sodium** 68mg
Carbohydrate 12g	

Exchanges: 1 starch, 1/2 fat

Cocoa-Cherry Chill

Lemon Pound Cake with Strawberries

(Pictured at right)

2 cups all-purpose flour
1 teaspoon baking powder
1 teaspoon baking soda
1/2 teaspoon salt
1/2 cup reduced-fat sour cream
1/2 cup fat-free milk
1/3 cup sugar
1/4 cup canola oil
1/4 cup egg substitute
2 tablespoons lemon juice
1 teaspoon grated lemon peel
3 pints fresh strawberries
Sugar substitute* (optional)

This recipe was tested with EQUAL® sweetener.

1. Preheat oven to 350°F. Coat 8×4-inch loaf pan with nonstick cooking spray; set aside.

2. Combine flour, baking powder, baking soda and salt in large bowl. Combine sour cream, milk, sugar, oil, egg substitute, lemon juice and lemon peel in medium bowl. Stir sour cream mixture into flour mixture until well combined; pour batter into prepared pan. Bake 45 to 50 minutes or until wooden toothpick inserted into center comes out clean.

3. Let cake cool 20 minutes before removing from pan; cool completely. Meanwhile, slice strawberries. Sprinkle to taste with sugar substitute, if desired. Cut cake into 16 slices and serve with strawberries.

Makes 16 servings

Nutrients per Serving: 1 slice cake with about 3 tablespoons sliced strawberries

Calories 180	**Fiber** 2g
Fat 6g (sat 1g)	**Cholesterol** 4mg
Protein 4g	**Sodium** 264mg
Carbohydrate 28g	

Exchanges: 1 starch, 1 fruit, 1 fat

Oatmeal-Molasses Cookies

1 cup whole wheat flour
1 cup all-purpose flour
1 teaspoon baking soda
1 teaspoon ground cinnamon
1/2 teaspoon salt
1/2 teaspoon ground ginger
1/2 cup granulated sugar
1/2 cup egg substitute
1/4 cup packed light brown sugar
1/4 cup (1/2 stick) butter
1/4 cup mild-flavored molasses
1 cup uncooked quick oats
1/2 cup raisins

1. Preheat oven to 350°F. Lightly spray baking sheet with nonstick cooking spray; set aside.

2. Combine whole wheat flour, all-purpose flour, baking soda, cinnamon, salt and ginger in medium bowl; set aside.

3. Combine granulated sugar, egg substitute, brown sugar, butter and molasses in large bowl with electric mixer at high speed until well blended. Add flour mixture. Stir in oats and raisins.

4. Drop dough by teaspoonfuls onto prepared baking sheet. Bake 10 minutes or until firm to touch. Remove to wire racks; cool completely.

Makes 36 servings

Nutrients per Serving: 1 cookie

Calories 71	**Fiber** 1g
Fat 2g (sat 1g)	**Cholesterol** 3mg
Protein 2g	**Sodium** 89mg
Carbohydrate 13g	

Exchanges: 1 starch

Lemon Pound Cake with Strawberries

Strawberry Granita

Strawberry Granita

(Pictured above)

1 quart fresh strawberries, sliced
1/4 cup powdered sugar
1/4 cup water
2 tablespoons sugar substitute*
1 to 1-1/2 tablespoons fresh lemon juice, divided

*This recipe was tested with SPLENDA® Granular.

1. Combine strawberries, powdered sugar, water, sugar substitute and 1 tablespoon lemon juice in blender container. Cover and purée. Taste; if too sweet, add additional 1/2 tablespoon lemon juice.

2. Pour mixture into metal 8-inch square pan. Cover pan with foil and place in freezer. Freeze granita 2 hours or until slushy. Remove from freezer and stir to break mixture up into small chunks. Cover and return to freezer. Freeze 2 hours, then stir to break granita up again. Cover and freeze at least 4 hours or overnight.

3. To serve, scrape surface of granita with large metal spoon to shave off thin pieces. Spoon into individual bowls. Serve immediately.

Makes 8 servings

Nutrients per Serving: 3/4 cup

Calories 54	**Fiber** 1g
Fat 0g (sat <1g)	**Cholesterol** 0mg
Protein <1g	**Sodium** 1mg
Carbohydrate 14g	

Exchanges: 1 fruit

Apricots and Cream

4 to 6 fresh apricots
2 cups unsweetened apple juice
1 stick cinnamon
1 cup 1% milk
3 tablespoons sugar
1 tablespoon cornstarch
1/4 teaspoon almond extract

1. Peel apricots; cut into halves and remove seeds. Combine apple juice and cinnamon in medium saucepan; bring to a boil over high heat. Reduce heat to low. Add apricots; simmer, uncovered, 5 minutes or until apricots are tender but firm. Drain and cool.

2. For cream sauce, combine milk, sugar and cornstarch in small saucepan until smooth. Cook and stir over medium-high heat until thickened. Stir in almond extract. Let sauce stand at room temperature until cooled. Refrigerate until ready to serve.

3. Pool 1/4 cup cream sauce on bottom of individual serving dish; arrange 2 to 3 apricot halves on top of sauce. Repeat with remaining apricots and sauce. *Makes 4 servings*

Nutrients per Serving: 1/4 cup sauce with 2 apricot halves

Calories 91	**Fiber** 1g
Fat 1g (sat <1g)	**Cholesterol** 3mg
Protein 3g	**Sodium** 32mg
Carbohydrate 19g	

Exchanges: 1 fruit, 1/2 milk

Chilled Cherry Cheesecake

(Pictured at bottom right)

> **4 chocolate graham crackers, crushed (about 1 cup crumbs)**
> **12 ounces reduced-fat cheese**
> **1 container (8 ounces) vanilla sugar-free fat-free yogurt**
> **1/4 cup sugar**
> **1 teaspoon vanilla extract**
> **1 envelope unflavored gelatin**
> **1/4 cup cold water**
> **1 can (20 ounces) light cherry pie filling**

1. Sprinkle graham cracker crumbs onto bottom of 8-inch square baking pan; set aside.

2. Beat cheese, yogurt, sugar and vanilla in medium bowl with electric mixer at medium speed until smooth and creamy.

3. Sprinkle gelatin into water in small cup; let stand 2 minutes. Microwave at HIGH 40 seconds; stir and let stand 2 minutes or until gelatin is completely dissolved.

4. Gradually beat gelatin mixture into cheese mixture with electric mixer at medium speed until well blended. Pour into prepared pan; refrigerate until firm.

5. Spoon cherry topping onto cheesecake. Refrigerate until ready to serve. Cut into 9 pieces to serve. *Makes 9 servings*

Nutrients per Serving: 1 piece cheesecake

Calories 221	**Fiber** 1g
Fat 10g (sat 6g)	**Cholesterol** 29mg
Protein 5g	**Sodium** 226mg
Carbohydrate 29g	

Exchanges: 2 starch, 1-1/2 fat

Tip

The best part about this cheesecake? It's versatile. Simply change the topping, and you have a completely different cheesecake. Blueberry and strawberry pie fillings are just a few others to try.

Angel Food Cake with Blueberry Yogurt Sauce

low fat

Quick Recipe

> **1/2 cup frozen blueberries**
> **Purchased small round angel food cake (12 ounces)**
> **1/2 cup vanilla nonfat yogurt**
> **3 teaspoons granulated sugar**
> **1 teaspoon lemon juice**

Allow blueberries to thaw slightly. Cut angel food cake into 12 slices. Stir together yogurt, sugar and lemon juice in small bowl. To serve, spoon yogurt mixture and blueberries evenly over cake slices. *Makes 12 servings*

Favorite recipe from **The Sugar Association, Inc.**

Nutrients per Serving: 1 (1-ounce) slice cake with about 2 teaspoons sauce and 2 teaspoons blueberries

Calories 84	**Fiber** 1g
Fat <1g (sat <1g)	**Cholesterol** <1mg
Protein 2g	**Sodium** 218mg
Carbohydrate 19g	

Exchanges: 1 starch

Chilled Cherry Cheesecake

Holiday Thumbprint Cookies

Quick Recipe   *(Pictured at right)*

> **1 package (8 ounces) yellow cake mix**
> **3 tablespoons orange juice**
> **2 teaspoons grated orange peel**
> **1/2 teaspoon vanilla extract**
> **5 teaspoons reduced-sugar strawberry fruit spread**
> **2 tablespoons chopped pecans**

1. Preheat oven to 350°F. Spray baking sheets with nonstick cooking spray; set aside.

2. Beat cake mix, orange juice, orange peel and vanilla in medium bowl with electric mixer at medium speed 2 minutes or until mixture looks crumbly. Increase speed to medium-high and beat 2 minutes or until smooth dough forms. (Dough will be very sticky.)

3. Spray hands with nonstick cooking spray. Roll dough into 1-inch balls. Place balls 2-1/2 inches apart on prepared baking sheets. Press center of each ball with thumb. Fill each thumbprint with 1/4 teaspoon fruit spread. Sprinkle with nuts.

4. Bake 8 to 9 minutes or until cookies are light golden brown and no longer shiny. *Do not overbake.* Remove to wire racks; cool completely.
Makes 20 servings

Nutrients per Serving: 1 cookie

Calories 54	**Fiber** <1g
Fat 1g (sat <1g)	**Cholesterol** 0mg
Protein <1g	**Sodium** 74mg
Carbohydrate 10g	

Exchanges: 1/2 starch, 1/2 fat

Pumpkin Roll

> **3 eggs**
> **1 cup EQUAL® SPOONFUL***
> **1 cup pumpkin**
> **1 teaspoon lemon juice**
> **1 cup self-rising flour**
> **2 teaspoons cinnamon**
> **1 teaspoon nutmeg**
> **4 ounces light cream cheese, softened**
> **1-1/2 to 2 cups light whipped topping**
> **2 tablespoons EQUAL® SPOONFUL** (or to taste)**

*May substitute 24 packets EQUAL® sweetener.

**May substitute 3 packets EQUAL® sweetener.

• Beat eggs and 1 cup Equal® Spoonful for 5 minutes in medium bowl.

• Stir in pumpkin and lemon juice; add flour, cinnamon and nutmeg. Mix well.

• Line jelly-roll pan with waxed paper. Spread batter evenly over pan. Bake in preheated 350°F oven 5 to 8 minutes or until toothpick comes out clean. Cool 3 minutes in pan; turn out onto cloth. Gently peel off waxed paper and roll up from narrow end.

• Chill in refrigerator until completely cool.

• For filling, mix cream cheese, whipped topping and 2 tablespoons Equal® Spoonful until smooth and spreadable.

• Unroll pumpkin roll and spread with filling. Re-roll and chill until serving time. Slice into pinwheels and serve.   *Makes 8 servings*

Nutrients per Serving: 1 pinwheel (1/8 of total recipe)

Calories 171	**Fiber** 2g
Fat 6g (sat 4g)	**Cholesterol** 88mg
Protein 6g	**Sodium** 277mg
Carbohydrate 23g	

Exchanges: 1-1/2 starch, 1 fat

Lighter Than Air Chocolate Delight

(Pictured at right)

2 envelopes unflavored gelatin
1/2 cup cold water
1 cup boiling water
1-1/3 cups nonfat dry milk powder
1/3 cup HERSHEY'S Cocoa or HERSHEY'S
　　Dutch Processed Cocoa
1 tablespoon vanilla extract
　Dash salt
　Granulated sugar substitute to equal
　　14 teaspoons sugar
8 large ice cubes

1. Sprinkle gelatin over cold water in blender container; let stand 4 minutes to soften. Gently stir with rubber spatula, scraping gelatin particles off sides; add boiling water to gelatin mixture. Cover; blend until gelatin dissolves. Add milk powder, cocoa, vanilla and salt; blend on medium speed until well mixed. Add sugar substitute and ice cubes; blend on high speed until ice is crushed and mixture is smooth and fluffy.

2. Immediately pour into 4-cup mold. Cover; refrigerate until firm. Unmold onto serving plate.　　　　　　　*Makes 8 servings*

Note: Eight individual dessert dishes may be used in place of 4-cup mold, if desired.

Nutrients per Serving: 1/2 cup

Calories 72	**Fiber** 1g
Fat <1g (sat <1g)	**Cholesterol** 2mg
Protein 6g	**Sodium** 67mg
Carbohydrate 10g	

Exchanges: 1 starch

Peach Custard

1/2 cup peeled fresh peach or nectarine, cut
　　into chunks
1 can (5 ounces) evaporated fat-free milk*
1/4 cup egg substitute
　Sugar substitute** equivalent to
　　2 teaspoons sugar
1/2 teaspoon vanilla extract
　Ground cinnamon

*If a 5-ounce can is not available, use 1/2 cup plus 2 tablespoons evaporated fat-free milk.

**This recipe was tested with EQUAL® sweetener.

1. Preheat oven to 325°F. Divide peach chunks between 2 (6-ounce) custard cups. Whisk together milk, egg substitute, sugar substitute and vanilla. Pour mixture over peach chunks in custard cups.

2. Place custard cups in shallow 1-quart casserole. Carefully pour hot water into casserole to depth of 1 inch. Bake custards 50 minutes or until knife inserted into custard centers comes out clean. Remove custard cups from water bath. Serve warm or at room temperature. Sprinkle with cinnamon.
　　　　　　　　　　Makes 2 servings

Note: Drained canned peach slices in juice can be substituted for fresh fruit.

Nutrients per Serving: 1 custard cup (1/2 of total recipe)

Calories 52	**Fiber** 1g
Fat <1g (sat <1g)	**Cholesterol** <1mg
Protein 5g	**Sodium** 71mg
Carbohydrate 7g	

Exchanges: 1/2 fruit, 1/2 lean meat

Lighter Than Air Chocolate Delight

Mint Chocolate Cups

Mint Chocolate Cups

(Pictured above)

> 2 packages (4-serving size each) sugar-free
> instant chocolate pudding and pie
> filling mix
> 2-1/2 cups fat-free half-and-half
> 1/2 cup fat-free sour cream
> 1 teaspoon vanilla extract
> 1/2 to 1 teaspoon peppermint extract
> 1-1/2 cups fat-free whipped topping
> 6 sugar-free peppermint patties, chopped

1. Whisk pudding mix with half-and-half in medium bowl. Blend with sour cream and vanilla and peppermint extracts until smooth.

2. Divide mixture evenly among 6 parfait glasses or dessert cups, spreading 2 tablespoons whipped topping in between to make layers. Top each with 2 tablespoons whipped topping. Chill 1 hour or until completely cold. Garnish each serving with 1 chopped sugar-free peppermint patty.

Makes 6 servings

Nutrients per Serving: 2/3 cup chocolate mixture with 1/4 cup whipped topping and 1 peppermint patty

Calories 166	**Fiber** <1g
Fat <1g (sat 0g)	**Cholesterol** 15mg
Protein 6g	**Sodium** 541mg
Carbohydrate 29g	

Exchanges: 1-1/2 starch, 1/2 milk

Berries and Sweet Cream Nesters

Quick Recipe

> 2 (14×9-inch) sheets phyllo dough
> Nonstick cooking spray
> 4 ounces reduced-fat cream cheese
> 1/4 cup reduced-fat sour cream
> 3 tablespoons fat-free milk
> 1 tablespoon sugar
> 3 packets sugar substitute*
> 1/2 teaspoon vanilla extract
> 1 cup fresh or frozen blueberries or
> raspberries, thawed

*This recipe was tested with SPLENDA® Granular.

1. Preheat oven to 350°F. Spray both sides of phyllo dough with cooking spray. Working quickly, cut each sheet of dough into 4 lengthwise strips, then cut each strip crosswise into fourths to make 32 squares total.

2. Spray nonstick muffin cups with cooking spray. Place 4 squares in each of 8 cups, with corners overlapping. Press down gently, so dough takes shape of cup. Ruffle edges to create nest appearance. Bake 4 minutes.

3. Remove muffin pan from oven. Cool nests in pan on wire rack before gently removing.

4. Meanwhile, beat cream cheese, sour cream, milk, sugar, sugar substitute and vanilla in medium bowl with electric mixer at medium speed until smooth.

5. To serve, spoon 2 tablespoons cream cheese mixture into each nest. Top each with 2 tablespoons berries. *Makes 8 servings*

Nutrients per Serving: 1 nest with 2 tablespoons filling and 2 tablespoons berries

Calories 75	**Fiber** <1g
Fat 3g (sat 2g)	**Cholesterol** 9mg
Protein 2g	**Sodium** 98mg
Carbohydrate 9g	

Exchanges: 1/2 starch, 1 fat

Chocolate Orange Cake Roll

(Pictured on page 150)

1/3 cup all-purpose flour
1/4 cup plus 1 tablespoon unsweetened
    cocoa powder, divided
1/4 teaspoon baking soda
  4 eggs, separated
1/2 teaspoon vanilla extract
1/2 cup plus 2 tablespoons sugar, divided
1/4 cup sugar substitute*
1/2 cup reduced-sugar orange fruit spread

This recipe was tested with SPLENDA® Granular.

1. Preheat oven to 375°F. Spray 15×10-inch jelly-roll pan with nonstick cooking spray. Dust with flour. Set aside.

2. Combine flour, 1/4 cup cocoa powder and baking soda in small bowl; set aside.

3. Beat 4 egg yolks and vanilla in large bowl with electric mixer at high speed 5 to 6 minutes or until thick and light colored. Gradually add 2 tablespoons sugar and sugar substitute, beating well after each addition.

4. Using clean beaters, beat 4 egg whites in another large bowl with electric mixer at high speed until soft peaks form. Gradually add remaining 1/2 cup sugar; beat until stiff peaks form.

5. Gently fold yolk mixture into egg white mixture. Sift flour mixture over egg mixture. Gently fold flour mixture into egg mixture just until combined. Spread evenly into prepared pan. Bake 12 to 15 minutes or until top springs back when lightly touched.

6. Meanwhile, sprinkle remaining 1 tablespoon cocoa powder onto one side of clean kitchen towel. Use narrow spatula to loosen edges of cake from pan. Invert pan onto prepared towel. Roll up towel and cake, starting from short side. Cool on wire rack. Unroll cake. Remove towel. Top cake with orange spread. Roll up cake. Cut into 10 slices before serving.

Makes 10 servings

Nutrients per Serving: 1 slice cake roll

Calories 136	**Fiber** 1g
Fat 2g (sat 1g)	**Cholesterol** 85mg
Protein 3g	**Sodium** 60mg
Carbohydrate 25g	

Exchanges: 1-1/2 starch, 1/2 fat

ᵒ ᵒ ᵒ

Lemon Whip

1 package (4-serving size) sugar-free
    lemon-flavored gelatin
1 cup boiling water
2 tablespoons fresh lemon juice
  Grated peel of 1 lemon
1 container (8 ounces) frozen fat-free
    whipped topping, thawed
1/4 cup powdered sugar
2 tablespoons sugar substitute*
2 tablespoons shredded coconut

This recipe was tested with SPLENDA® Granular.

1. Place gelatin in heat-proof bowl. Stir in boiling water to dissolve gelatin. Mix lemon juice with enough cold water to equal 1 cup. Stir into gelatin. Stir in lemon peel. Chill in refrigerator 2 hours or until semi-firm. Beat gently to break into pieces.

2. Fold in whipped topping, powdered sugar and sugar substitute; beat with whisk until fluffy. Spoon into dessert bowl. Top with shredded coconut. Serve immediately.

Makes 6 servings

Hint: Toast coconut for added flavor, if desired. Spread coconut on baking sheet. Toast in preheated 400°F oven for 5 minutes.

Nutrients per Serving: 3/4 cup

Calories 141	**Fiber** <1g
Fat 7g (sat 7g)	**Cholesterol** 0mg
Protein 1g	**Sodium** 38mg
Carbohydrate 15g	

Exchanges: 1 starch, 1-1/2 fat

Pumpkin Pie

(Pictured at right)

Pastry for single-crust 9-inch pie
1 can (16 ounces) pumpkin
1 can (12 ounces) evaporated fat-free
   milk
3 eggs
3/4 cup EQUAL® SPOONFUL*
1 teaspoon vanilla
1 teaspoon ground cinnamon
1/4 teaspoon ground ginger
1/4 teaspoon ground nutmeg
1/4 teaspoon salt

May substitute 18 packets EQUAL® sweetener.

• Roll pastry on floured surface into circle
1 inch larger than inverted 9-inch pie pan. Ease
pastry into pie pan; trim and flute edge.

• Beat pumpkin, evaporated milk and eggs in
medium bowl; beat in remaining ingredients.
Pour into pastry shell. Bake in preheated 400°F
oven 35 to 40 minutes or until knife inserted
into center comes out clean.

• Cool on wire rack.   *Makes 8 servings*

Hint: Instead of fluting the edge, cut out
decorative shapes from any remaining pie crust
dough and use them to trim the edge of the pie.

Nutrients per Serving: 1 slice pie (1/8 of total recipe)

Calories 175	**Fiber** 1g
Fat 7g (sat 4g)	**Cholesterol** 86mg
Protein 8g	**Sodium** 208mg
Carbohydrate 22g	

Exchanges: 1 starch, 1/2 milk, 1/2 lean meat, 1/2 fat

Hikers' Bar Cookies

Quick Recipe

3/4 cup all-purpose flour
1/2 cup packed brown sugar
1/2 cup uncooked quick oats
1/4 cup toasted wheat germ
1/4 cup unsweetened applesauce
1/4 cup (1/2 stick) butter, softened
1/8 teaspoon salt
1/2 cup egg substitute
1/4 cup raisins
1/4 cup dried cranberries
1/4 cup sunflower kernels
1 tablespoon grated orange peel
1 teaspoon ground cinnamon

1. Preheat oven to 350°F. Lightly spray
13×9-inch baking dish with nonstick cooking
spray; set aside.

2. Beat flour, brown sugar, oats, wheat germ,
applesauce, butter and salt in large bowl with
electric mixer at medium speed until well
blended. Add egg substitute, raisins, cranberries,
sunflower kernels, orange peel and cinnamon.
Spread into prepared dish.

3. Bake 15 minutes or until firm to touch. Cool
completely in dish. Cut into 24 bars.
          Makes 24 servings

Nutrients per Serving: 1 bar

Calories 80	**Fiber** 1g
Fat 3g (sat 1g)	**Cholesterol** 5mg
Protein 2g	**Sodium** 46mg
Carbohydrate 12g	

Exchanges: 1 starch, 1/2 fat

Pumpkin Pie

Chocolate-Strawberry Crêpes

(Pictured on page 150)

Crêpes

  2/3 cup all-purpose flour
  2 tablespoons unsweetened cocoa powder
    Sugar substitute* equivalent to 1/4 cup sugar
  1/4 teaspoon salt
  1-1/4 cups fat-free milk
  1/2 cup egg substitute *or* 4 egg whites
  1 tablespoon butter, melted
  1 teaspoon vanilla extract

Filling and Topping

  4 ounces fat-free cream cheese, softened
  1 package (4-serving size) sugar-free instant chocolate-fudge-flavored pudding and pie filling mix
  1-1/2 cups fat-free milk
  1/4 cup reduced-sugar strawberry preserves
  2 tablespoons water
  2 cups hulled and quartered fresh strawberries

This recipe was tested with EQUAL® sweetener.

1. For crêpes, combine flour, cocoa, sugar substitute and salt in food processor; cover and process. Add milk, egg substitute, butter and vanilla; process until smooth. Let stand at room temperature 30 minutes.

2. Spray 7-inch nonstick skillet with nonstick cooking spray; heat over medium-high heat. Pour 2 tablespoons batter into hot skillet. Immediately rotate skillet back and forth to swirl batter over entire surface. Cook 1 to 2 minutes or until crêpe is brown around edge and top is dry. Carefully turn crêpe with spatula and cook 30 seconds more. Transfer crêpe to waxed paper to cool. Repeat with remaining batter, spraying skillet with cooking spray as needed. Separate crêpes with sheets of waxed paper.

3. For chocolate filling, beat cream cheese in medium bowl with electric mixer at high speed until smooth; set aside. Prepare chocolate pudding with skim milk according to package directions. Gradually add pudding to cream cheese; beat at high speed 3 minutes.

4. For strawberry topping, combine preserves and water in large bowl until smooth. Add strawberries; toss to coat.

5. Spread 2 tablespoons chocolate filling evenly over surface of crêpe; roll tightly. Repeat with remaining crêpes. Serve with strawberry topping.   *Makes 8 servings*

Nutrients per Serving: 2 crêpes with 1/4 cup strawberry topping (2 tablespoons per crêpe)

Calories 149	**Fiber** 2g
Fat 2g (sat 1g)	**Cholesterol** 7mg
Protein 8g	**Sodium** 390mg
Carbohydrate 24g	

Exchanges: 1 starch, 1/2 fruit, 1/2 milk

Crunchy Peanut Butter Balls

Quick Recipe

  1/2 cup cornstarch
  1/2 cup peanut butter
  1 cup dry puffed rice cereal
  1 tablespoon chocolate chips
  1-1/8 tablespoons sugar substitute*
  1/4 cup cold water

This recipe was tested with SPLENDA® Granular.

Mix all ingredients in medium bowl. Form mixture into 8 balls of equal size. Refrigerate in airtight container.   *Makes 8 servings*

Nutrients per Serving: 1 ball

Calories 141	**Fiber** 1g
Fat 9g (sat 2g)	**Cholesterol** 0mg
Protein 4g	**Sodium** 81mg
Carbohydrate 13g	

Exchanges: 1 starch, 1-1/2 fat

Pumpkin Polka Dot Cookies

1-1/4 cups EQUAL® SPOONFUL*

1/2 cup stick butter or margarine, softened

3 tablespoons light molasses

1 cup canned pumpkin

1 egg

1-1/2 teaspoons vanilla

1-2/3 cups all-purpose flour

1 teaspoon baking powder

1-1/4 teaspoons ground cinnamon

1/2 teaspoon ground nutmeg

1/2 teaspoon ground ginger

1/2 teaspoon baking soda

1/4 teaspoon salt

1 cup mini semi-sweet chocolate chips

*May substitute 30 packets EQUAL® sweetener.

• Beat Equal®, butter and molasses until well combined. Mix in pumpkin, egg and vanilla until blended. Gradually stir in combined flour, baking powder, spices, baking soda and salt until well blended. Stir in chocolate chips.

• Drop by teaspoonfuls onto baking sheet sprayed with nonstick cooking spray. Bake in preheated 350°F oven 11 to 13 minutes. Remove from baking sheet and cool completely on wire rack. Store at room temperature in airtight container up to 1 week.

Makes about 4 dozen cookies

Nutrients per Serving: 1 cookie

Calories 63	**Fiber** 1g
Fat 3g (sat 2g)	**Cholesterol** 10mg
Protein 1g	**Sodium** 69mg
Carbohydrate 8g	

Exchanges: 1/2 starch, 1/2 fat

Cranberry Orange Cheesecake

1-1/3 cups gingersnap crumbs

3 tablespoons EQUAL® SPOONFUL*

3 tablespoons stick butter or margarine, melted

3 packages (8 ounces each) reduced-fat cream cheese, softened

1 cup EQUAL® SPOONFUL**

2 eggs

2 egg whites

2 tablespoons cornstarch

1/4 teaspoon salt

1 cup reduced-fat sour cream

2 teaspoons vanilla

1 cup chopped fresh or frozen cranberries

1-1/2 teaspoons grated orange peel

*May substitute 4-1/2 packets EQUAL® sweetener.

**May substitute 24 packets EQUAL® sweetener.

• Mix gingersnap crumbs, 3 tablespoons Equal® and melted butter in bottom of 9-inch springform pan. Reserve 2 tablespoons crumb mixture. Pat remaining mixture evenly onto bottom of pan. Bake in preheated 325°F oven 8 minutes. Cool on wire rack.

• Beat cream cheese and 1 cup Equal® in large bowl until fluffy; beat in eggs, egg whites, cornstarch and salt. Beat in sour cream and vanilla until blended. Gently stir in cranberries and orange peel. Pour batter into crust in pan. Sprinkle with reserved crumb mixture.

• Bake in 325°F oven 45 to 50 minutes or until center is almost set. Remove cheesecake to wire rack. Gently run metal spatula around rim of pan to loosen cake. Let cheesecake cool completely. Cover and refrigerate several hours or overnight before serving. To serve, remove sides of springform pan. *Makes 16 servings*

Nutrients per Serving: 1 slice (1/16 of total recipe)

Calories 193	**Fiber** 1g
Fat 11g (sat 7g)	**Cholesterol** 57mg
Protein 7g	**Sodium** 331mg
Carbohydrate 14g	

Exchanges: 1 starch, 1/2 lean meat, 2 fat

Streusel-Topped Strawberry Cheesecake Square

Streusel-Topped Strawberry Cheesecake Squares

(Pictured above)

- **1 container (8 ounces) strawberry fat-free yogurt with aspartame sweetener**
- **1 package (8 ounces) fat-free cream cheese**
- **4 ounces reduced-fat cream cheese**
  Sugar substitute* equivalent to 1/4 cup sugar
- **1 packet unflavored gelatin**
- **2 tablespoons water**
- **1 cup chopped fresh strawberries**
- **1 tablespoon sugar**
- **1 cup sliced fresh strawberries**
- **1/3 cup reduced-fat granola**

*This recipe was tested with EQUAL® sweetener.

1. Line 9-inch square baking pan with plastic wrap, leaving 4-inch overhang on 2 opposite sides.

2. Combine yogurt, cream cheese and sugar substitute in medium bowl; beat until smooth. Set aside.

3. Combine gelatin and water in small microwavable bowl; let stand 2 minutes. Microwave at HIGH 40 seconds to dissolve gelatin. Beat gelatin into yogurt mixture.

4. Combine chopped strawberries and sugar in small bowl. Add to yogurt mixture.

5. Pour yogurt mixture evenly into prepared pan. Refrigerate 1 hour or until firm.

6. Just before serving, arrange sliced strawberries on top. Sprinkle with granola.

7. Gently lift cheesecake out of pan with plastic wrap. Pull plastic wrap away from sides. Cut cheesecake into 9 squares.

Makes 9 servings

Nutrients per Serving: 1 cheesecake square

Calories 98	**Fiber** 1g
Fat 3g (sat 2g)	**Cholesterol** 8mg
Protein 7g	**Sodium** 223mg
Carbohydrate 11g	

Exchanges: 1/2 starch, 1/2 fruit, 1/2 fat

Tip

When shopping for fresh strawberries, look for shiny, bright red, fragrant berries with vibrant green caps. Strawberries do not ripen off the vine, so be sure to avoid green or pale red (underripe) berries. Check the berries for soft spots, mildew and leakage—all signs of deterioration. Unwashed strawberries, with stems and caps still attached, can be stored in the refrigerator for up to 3 days. Just before using the berries, quickly and gently wash them under cold running water. Leave the caps on for this wash, or the berries will absorb some of the water, causing them to soften. About 1/2 pound or 1/2 pint of strawberries yields 1 cup of strawberry slices.

Lemon Meringue Pie

(Pictured on page 150)

Pastry for single-crust 9-inch pie
2-1/4 cups water
1/2 cup fresh lemon juice or frozen lemon juice concentrate*
1/2 cup cornstarch
2 eggs
2 egg whites
1-1/2 teaspoons grated lemon peel
1-1/2 cups EQUAL® SPOONFUL**
2 tablespoons stick butter or margarine
1 to 2 drops yellow food coloring (optional)
3 egg whites
1/4 teaspoon cream of tartar
2/3 cup EQUAL® SPOONFUL***

*Such as Minute Maid® Premium Lemon Juice (frozen) 100% Pure Lemon Juice from Concentrate

**May substitute 36 packets EQUAL® sweetener.

***May substitute 16 packets EQUAL® sweetener.

• Roll pastry on lightly floured surface into circle 1 inch larger than inverted 9-inch pie pan. Ease pastry into pan; trim and flute edge. Pierce bottom and side of pastry with fork. Bake in preheated 425°F oven 10 to 12 minutes or until pastry is golden. Cool on wire rack.

• Combine water, lemon juice and cornstarch in medium saucepan. Bring to a boil over medium-high heat, stirring constantly; boil and stir 1 minute. Beat eggs, 2 egg whites and lemon peel in medium bowl. Mix in 1-1/2 cups Equal® Spoonful. Stir about half of hot cornstarch mixture into egg mixture.

• Return all to saucepan. Cook and stir over low heat 1 minute. Remove from heat; stir in butter until melted. Stir in food coloring, if desired. Pour mixture into baked pie shell.

• Beat 3 egg whites in medium bowl until foamy. Add cream of tartar and beat to soft peaks. Gradually beat in 2/3 cup Equal® Spoonful, beating to stiff peaks. Spread meringue over hot lemon filling, carefully sealing to edge of crust to prevent shrinking or weeping.

• Bake pie in 425°F oven about 5 minutes or until meringue is lightly browned. Cool completely before cutting. *Makes 8 servings*

Nutrients per Serving: 1 slice pie (1/8 of total recipe)

Calories 189	Fiber 1g
Fat 10g (sat 4g)	Cholesterol 61mg
Protein 5g	Sodium 228mg
Carbohydrate 19g	

Exchanges: 1-1/2 starch, 1-1/2 fat

Special Crunchy Cookies

1 cup EQUAL® SPOONFUL*
1/2 cup stick butter or margarine, softened
1 egg
1 teaspoon vanilla
4 cups Kellogg's® Special K® cereal, crushed to 1-1/2 cups, divided
1 cup all-purpose flour
1 teaspoon baking powder
1/4 teaspoon salt
1/2 cup mini semi-sweet chocolate chips

*May substitute 24 packets EQUAL® sweetener.

• Beat Equal® and butter on medium speed of electric mixer until light and fluffy. Beat in egg and vanilla until well combined.

• Stir in combined 1 cup crushed cereal, flour, baking powder and salt until well blended. Stir in chocolate chips. Shape dough into balls using rounded measuring teaspoons. Roll in remaining 1/2 cup crushed cereal. Place on ungreased baking sheet.

• Bake in preheated 375°F oven 8 to 10 minutes. Remove from baking sheet and cool completely on wire rack. *Makes about 4 dozen cookies*

Nutrients per Serving: 2 cookies

Calories 92	Fiber <1g
Fat 6g (sat 3g)	Cholesterol 20mg
Protein 2g	Sodium 128mg
Carbohydrate 10g	

Exchanges: 1/2 starch, 1 fat

Watermelon Ice

(Pictured at right)

**4 cups seeded 1-inch watermelon cubes
1/4 cup thawed frozen unsweetened
pineapple juice concentrate
2 tablespoons fresh lime juice
Fresh melon balls (optional)**

1. Place melon chunks in single layer in plastic freezer bag; freeze until firm, about 8 hours.

2. Place frozen melon in food processor container fitted with steel blade. Let stand 15 minutes to soften slightly. Add pineapple juice and lime juice. Remove plunger from top of food processor to allow air to be incorporated. Process until smooth, scraping down sides of container frequently.

3. Spoon into individual dessert dishes. Garnish with melon balls, if desired. Freeze leftovers.
Makes 6 servings

Honeydew Ice: Substitute honeydew for watermelon and unsweetened pineapple-guava-orange juice concentrate for pineapple juice concentrate.

Cantaloupe Ice: Substitute cantaloupe for watermelon and unsweetened pineapple-guava-orange juice concentrate for pineapple juice concentrate.

Note: Ices can be transferred to an airtight container and frozen up to 1 month. Let stand at room temperature 10 minutes to soften slightly before serving.

Nutrients per Serving: 1/2 cup Watermelon Ice

Calories 57	**Fiber** 1g
Fat <1g (sat <1g)	**Cholesterol** 0mg
Protein 1g	**Sodium** 3mg
Carbohydrate 13g	

Exchanges: 1 fruit

Speed Dial Fruit Cobbler

Quick Recipe

**1/2 cup frozen blueberries, partially thawed
1/2 cup frozen raspberries, partially thawed
1-1/2 cups frozen unsweetened peaches,
partially thawed and diced
2 tablespoons reduced-sugar apricot fruit
spread
Sugar substitute* equivalent to
2 teaspoons sugar
1/8 teaspoon almond extract
8 shortbread cookies, coarsely crushed**

*This recipe was tested with SPLENDA® Granular.

1. Place equal amount of blueberries and raspberries in each of 4 (4-ounce) glass dishes; set aside.

2. Combine peaches and fruit spread in medium saucepan. Heat over medium heat, stirring frequently, until spread is melted and just begins to boil.

3. Remove from heat; stir in sugar substitute and almond extract. Immediately spoon over berries. Top with cookie crumbs. *Makes 4 servings*

Nutrients per Serving: 1/2 cup cobbler

Calories 106	**Fiber** 2g
Fat 2g (sat <1g)	**Cholesterol** 0mg
Protein 1g	**Sodium** 39mg
Carbohydrate 23g	

Exchanges: 1/2 starch, 1 fruit, 1/2 fat

Tip

A 4-pound watermelon yields about 4 cups of watermelon cubes.

*Clockwise from top left:
Watermelon Ice,
Honeydew Ice and
Cantaloupe Ice*

Raspberry Buckle

(Pictured at right)

1-1/4 cups all-purpose flour
1/2 cup plus 2 tablespoons sugar substitute,*
divided
2 tablespoons granulated sugar
1-1/4 teaspoons baking powder
1/4 teaspoon *each* baking soda and salt
2/3 cup buttermilk
1/4 cup plus 2 tablespoons egg substitute,
divided
2 tablespoons butter, melted
1 teaspoon vanilla extract
2 ounces reduced-fat cream cheese,
softened
1-1/4 cups fresh or frozen raspberries, thawed
1 tablespoon powdered sugar

*This recipe was tested with SPLENDA® Granular.

1. Preheat oven to 375°F. Lightly spray 9-inch round baking pan with nonstick cooking spray; set aside.

2. Combine flour, 1/2 cup sugar substitute, granulated sugar, baking powder, baking soda and salt in large bowl. Combine buttermilk, 1/4 cup egg substitute, butter and vanilla in small bowl; add to flour mixture. Stir to combine. Spread into prepared pan.

3. Beat cream cheese and remaining 2 tablespoons sugar substitute in small bowl with electric mixer at medium speed until combined. Beat in remaining 2 tablespoons egg substitute.

4. Sprinkle raspberries over batter in pan. Dollop cheese mixture over top. Bake 30 to 33 minutes or until wooden toothpick inserted into center comes out clean. Remove to wire rack. Cool 10 minutes. Sprinkle with powdered sugar. Serve warm. *Makes 8 servings*

Nutrients per Serving: 1 piece (1/8 of total recipe)

Calories 185	**Fiber** 2g
Fat 5g (sat 3g)	**Cholesterol** 13mg
Protein 5g	**Sodium** 241mg
Carbohydrate 38g	

Exchanges: 2 starch, 1/2 fruit, 1/2 fat

Deep, Dark Gingerbread Rounds

 low fat

1 package (14.5 ounces) gingerbread cake
and cookie mix
2 cans (8 ounces each) crushed pineapple
in juice, drained
2 jars (4 ounces each) baby food puréed
sweet potatoes
2 egg whites *or* 1/4 cup egg substitute
1/2 cup reduced-fat cream cheese

1. Preheat oven to 325°F. Spray 24 nonstick muffin cups with nonstick cooking spray; set aside.

2. Combine cake mix, pineapple, sweet potatoes and egg whites in medium bowl; stir until just blended.

3. Spoon equal amount of batter into each prepared muffin cup. Bake 25 minutes or until wooden toothpick inserted into centers comes out clean.

4. Remove to wire racks; cool completely.

5. To serve, top each cake round with 1 teaspoon cream cheese. *Makes 24 servings*

Note: These cake rounds taste even better the day after they're made.

Nutrients per Serving: 1 round with 1 teaspoon cream cheese

Calories 105	**Fiber** 1g
Fat 3g (sat 1g)	**Cholesterol** 3mg
Protein 2g	**Sodium** 144mg
Carbohydrate 17g	

Exchanges: 1 starch, 1/2 fat

Raspberry Buckle

Double Chocolate Brownies

Double Chocolate Brownies

low sodium low carb

Quick Recipe   *(Pictured above)*

 1 cup EQUAL® SPOONFUL*
 3/4 cup all-purpose flour
 1/2 cup semi-sweet chocolate chips or mini
     chocolate chips
 6 tablespoons unsweetened cocoa
 1 teaspoon baking powder
 1/4 teaspoon salt
 6 tablespoons stick butter or margarine,
     softened
 1/2 cup unsweetened applesauce
 2 eggs
 1 teaspoon vanilla

May substitute 24 packets EQUAL® sweetener.

• Combine Equal®, flour, chocolate chips, cocoa, baking powder and salt. Beat butter, applesauce, eggs and vanilla until blended. Stir in combined flour mixture until blended.

• Spread batter in 8-inch square baking pan sprayed with nonstick cooking spray. Bake in preheated 350°F oven 18 to 20 minutes or until top springs back when gently touched. Cool completely on wire rack.   *Makes 16 servings*

Nutrients per Serving: 1 brownie (1/16 of total recipe)

Calories 108	**Fiber** 1g
Fat 7g (sat 4g)	**Cholesterol** 38mg
Protein 2g	**Sodium** 119mg
Carbohydrate 10g	

Exchanges: 1 starch, 1 fat

Cinnamon Raisin Bread Pudding

 2 cups fat-free milk
 2/3 cup EQUAL® SPOONFUL*
 4 tablespoons stick butter or margarine,
     melted
 1 egg
 2 egg whites
 1 teaspoon cinnamon
 1/4 teaspoon salt
 4 cups (3/4-inch cubes) day-old
     cinnamon raisin bread

May substitute 16 packets EQUAL® sweetener.

• Combine milk, Equal®, melted butter, egg, egg whites, cinnamon and salt in large bowl. Stir in bread cubes.

• Spoon mixture into ungreased 1-1/2-quart rectangular casserole. Bake in preheated 350°F oven 30 to 35 minutes or until pudding is set and sharp knife inserted near center comes out clean.   *Makes 6 servings*

Nutrients per Serving: 1/2 cup plus 2 tablespoons pudding

Calories 232	**Fiber** 2g
Fat 10g (sat 2g)	**Cholesterol** 37mg
Protein 10g	**Sodium** 405mg
Carbohydrate 26g	

Exchanges: 1-1/2 starch, 1/2 milk, 1/2 lean meat, 1-1/2 fat

Crème Caramel

(Pictured at bottom right)

1/2 cup sugar, divided
1 tablespoon hot water
2 cups fat-free milk
1/8 teaspoon salt
1/2 cup egg substitute
1/2 teaspoon vanilla extract
1/8 teaspoon maple extract

1. Heat 1/4 cup sugar in heavy saucepan over low heat, stirring constantly until melted and straw-colored. Remove from heat; stir in water. Return to heat; cook and stir 5 minutes or until mixture is dark caramel color. Divide melted sugar evenly among 6 custard cups. Set aside.

2. Preheat oven to 350°F. Combine milk, remaining 1/4 cup sugar and salt in medium bowl. Add egg substitute, vanilla and maple extract; mix well. Pour 1/2 cup mixture into each custard cup. Place cups in heavy baking pan and pour 1 to 2 inches hot water into pan.

3. Bake 40 to 45 minutes or until knife inserted near edge of each cup comes out clean. Cool on wire rack. Refrigerate 4 hours or overnight. Before serving, run knife around edge of custard cup. Invert custard onto serving plate; remove cup.

Makes 6 servings

Nutrients per Serving: 1 custard cup

Calories 113	**Fiber** 0g
Fat 1g (sat <1g)	**Cholesterol** 1mg
Protein 5g	**Sodium** 130mg
Carbohydrate 21g	

Exchanges: 1 starch, 1/2 milk

Tip

A hot water bath, such as the one used in this recipe, provides a constant, steady heat source to the food, ensuring even cooking. Immediately remove the custard from the water bath after it passes the doneness test. If overcooked or cooked without the hot water bath, the custard will become rubbery.

Coffee Granita

2 cups water
1-1/2 tablespoons freeze-dried coffee granules
1/4 cup powdered sugar
2 tablespoons sugar substitute*
5 tablespoons fat-free whipped topping

This recipe was tested with SPLENDA® Granular.

1. Combine water, coffee, powdered sugar and sugar substitute in small saucepan. Bring to a boil over medium-high heat and stir to dissolve completely.

2. Pour into metal 8-inch square pan. Cover pan with foil and place in freezer. Freeze granita 2 hours or until slushy. Remove from freezer and stir to break mixture up into small chunks. Cover and return to freezer. Freeze 2 hours, then stir to break granita up again. Cover and freeze at least 4 hours or overnight.

3. To serve, scrape surface of granita with large metal spoon to shave off thin pieces. Spoon into individual bowls and top each serving with 1 tablespoon whipped topping. Serve immediately.

Makes 5 servings

Nutrients per Serving: 3/4 cup Granita

Calories 42	**Fiber** 0g
Fat 1g (sat 1g)	**Cholesterol** 0mg
Protein <1g	**Sodium** 1mg
Carbohydrate 8g	

Exchanges: 1/2 starch

Crème Caramel

Triple Berry Tart

(Pictured at right)

1 unbaked refrigerated (9-inch) pie crust
1/4 cup reduced-sugar raspberry fruit
    spread
1-1/2 cups fat-free whipped topping
3 ounces reduced-fat cream cheese,
    softened
1-1/2 cups fresh strawberry halves or
    quarters, stemmed
1/2 cup fresh raspberries
1-1/3 cups fresh or frozen blueberries,
    thawed
1 tablespoon powdered sugar

1. Preheat oven to 450°F.

2. Unroll pie crust on large nonstick baking sheet; prick with fork. Bake 8 minutes or until light brown. Remove to wire rack; cool completely.

3. Place fruit spread in small microwavable bowl; microwave at HIGH 15 seconds or until slightly melted. Remove from microwave. Spread evenly over pie crust, leaving 1/2-inch border.

4. Beat whipped topping with cream cheese in medium bowl with electric mixer on medium speed until well blended and smooth. Spoon tablespoonfuls whipped topping mixture evenly over fruit spread. Using back of spoon, smooth whipped topping layer.

5. Arrange berries in decorative fashion over top. Sprinkle with powdered sugar.

Makes 8 servings

Nutrients per Serving: 1 wedge (1/8 of total recipe)

Calories 180	**Fiber** 2g
Fat 7g (sat 2g)	**Cholesterol** 6mg
Protein 2g	**Sodium** 143mg
Carbohydrate 26g	

Exchanges: 1 starch, 1 fruit, 1-1/2 fat

Fresh Lemon Cheesecake with Raspberries

4 ounces fat-free cream cheese
2 ounces reduced-fat cream cheese
1/2 cup sugar
1 teaspoon vanilla extract
1/2 cup egg substitute
2 tablespoons lemon juice
2 teaspoons grated lemon peel, divided
1 container (8 ounces) fat-free sour cream
Sugar substitute* equivalent to
    10 teaspoons sugar, divided
2 cups raspberries or other berries

This recipe was tested with EQUAL® sweetener.

1. Preheat oven to 350°F. Spray 8-inch square baking pan with nonstick cooking spray; set aside.

2. Beat cream cheese, sugar and vanilla in large bowl with electric mixer at high speed until smooth. Add egg substitute, lemon juice and 1 teaspoon lemon peel; beat until well blended. Pour into prepared pan. Bake 40 minutes or until firm to touch. Cool completely in pan on wire rack.

3. Combine sour cream and 6 teaspoons sugar substitute in medium bowl; whisk until smooth. Spoon sour cream mixture over cooled cheesecake, smoothing evenly over top; refrigerate overnight.

4. Toss raspberries with remaining 4 teaspoons sugar substitute 30 minutes before serving; let stand at room temperature. Just before serving, toss berries with remaining 1 teaspoon lemon peel. Spoon berry mixture on top of cheesecake.

Makes 12 servings

Nutrients per Serving: 1 slice cheesecake with about 2 tablespoons plus 2 teaspoons berry topping

Calories 143	**Fiber** 1g
Fat 5g (sat 3g)	**Cholesterol** 14mg
Protein 7g	**Sodium** 218mg
Carbohydrate 17g	

Exchanges: 1 starch, 1/2 lean meat, 1 fat

Rustic Peach Oat Crumble

(Pictured at right)

4 cups frozen unsweetened peaches,
thawed and juices reserved

1/4 cup packed dark brown sugar

1 tablespoon cornstarch

1 to 2 tablespoons water

1 tablespoon lemon juice (optional)

1 teaspoon vanilla extract

1/4 teaspoon almond extract

1/2 cup uncooked quick oats

2 tablespoons all-purpose flour

2 tablespoons sugar substitute*

1/2 to 3/4 teaspoon ground cinnamon

1/8 teaspoon salt

1/4 cup (1/2 stick) cold reduced-fat butter,
cut into small pieces

Fat-free whipped topping (optional)

*This recipe was tested with SPLENDA® Granular.

1. Preheat oven to 375°F. Spray 9-inch pie plate
with nonstick cooking spray; set aside.

2. Combine peaches with juices, brown sugar,
cornstarch, water, lemon juice, if desired,
vanilla and almond extract in medium bowl.
Toss until cornstarch is completely dissolved.
Transfer to prepared pie plate.

3. Combine oats, flour, sugar substitute,
cinnamon and salt in medium bowl. Cut in
butter with pastry blender or two knives until
mixture resembles coarse crumbs. Crumble
evenly over peaches. Bake 25 minutes or until
peaches are bubbly at edges. Remove to wire
rack. Let stand 20 minutes. Top each serving
with dollop of whipped cream, if desired.

Makes 8 servings

Nutrients per Serving: 1/2 cup crumble

Calories 146	**Fiber** 2g
Fat 6g (sat 4g)	**Cholesterol** 15mg
Protein 2g	**Sodium** 41mg
Carbohydrate 24g	

Exchanges: 1/2 starch, 1 fruit, 1 fat

Citrus Sorbet

1 can (12 ounces) DOLE® Orange Peach
Mango or Tropical Fruit Frozen Juice
Concentrate

1 can (8 ounces) DOLE® Crushed
Pineapple or Pineapple Tidbits,
drained

1/2 cup plain nonfat or low fat yogurt

2-1/2 cups cold water

• Combine frozen juice concentrate, crushed
pineapple and yogurt in blender or food
processor container; blend until smooth. Stir in
water.

• Pour mixture into container of ice cream
maker.* Freeze according to manufacturer's
directions.

• Serve sorbet in dessert dishes.

Makes 10 servings

**Or, pour sorbet mixture into 8-inch square metal pan; cover.
Freeze 1-1/2 to 2 hours or until slightly firm. Remove to large
bowl; beat with electric mixer on medium speed 1 minute or
until slushy. Return mixture to metal pan; repeat freezing and
beating steps. Freeze until firm, about 6 hours or overnight.*

Passion-Banana Sorbet: Substitute DOLE® Pine-
Orange-Banana Frozen Juice Concentrate for
frozen juice concentrate. Prepare sorbet as
directed above except reduce water to 2 cups
and omit canned pineapple.

Nutrients per Serving: about 1 cup sorbet

Calories 86	**Fiber** <1g
Fat <1g (sat <1g)	**Cholesterol** <1mg
Protein 1g	**Sodium** 22mg
Carbohydrate 21g	

Exchanges: 1-1/2 fruit

Rustic Peach Oat Crumble

Tangy Lemon Squares

Tangy Lemon Squares

low sodium low carb

(Pictured above)

3/4 cup all-purpose flour
1/3 cup EQUAL® SPOONFUL*
1/8 teaspoon salt
  6 tablespoons cold stick butter or margarine, cut into pieces
  1 teaspoon grated lemon peel
  1 teaspoon vanilla
  2 eggs
3/4 cup EQUAL® SPOONFUL**
1/2 cup lemon juice
  4 tablespoons stick butter or margarine, melted
  1 tablespoon grated lemon peel

May substitute 8 packets EQUAL® sweetener.

**May substitute 18 packets EQUAL® sweetener.*

• Combine flour, 1/3 cup Equal® Spoonful and salt in medium bowl. Cut in 6 tablespoons butter with pastry blender until mixture resembles coarse crumbs. Sprinkle with 1 teaspoon lemon peel and vanilla; mix with hands to form dough.

• Press dough evenly onto bottom and 1/4 inch up sides of 8-inch square baking pan. Bake in preheated 350°F oven 8 to 10 minutes. Cool on wire rack.

• Beat eggs and 3/4 cup Equal® Spoonful; mix in lemon juice, 4 tablespoons butter and 1 tablespoon lemon peel. Pour mixture into baked pastry.

• Bake until lemon filling is set, about 15 minutes. Cool completely on wire rack.

Makes 16 servings

Nutrients per Serving: 1 square (1/16 of total recipe)

Calories 97	**Fiber** <1g
Fat 8g (sat 4g)	**Cholesterol** 46mg
Protein 2g	**Sodium** 101mg
Carbohydrate 5g	

Exchanges: 1/2 starch, 1-1/2 fat

Toasted Coconut and Tropical Fruit Parfait

low fat low sodium

Quick Recipe

  2 tablespoons flaked sweetened coconut
  1 cup pineapple sherbet
  1 cup diced strawberries
3/4 cup diced peeled mango or peaches
  1 kiwifruit, peeled and diced

1. Heat small skillet over medium-high heat until hot. Add coconut; cook and stir 1 to 1-1/2 minutes or until golden, stirring constantly. Remove from heat; set aside.

2. Spoon 1/4 cup sherbet into each of 4 parfait glasses. Top with strawberries, mango and kiwifruit. Sprinkle coconut over top.

Makes 4 servings

Nutrients per Serving: 3/4 cup

Calories 110	**Fiber** 3g
Fat 2g (sat 1g)	**Cholesterol** 0mg
Protein 1g	**Sodium** 45mg
Carbohydrate 25g	

Exchanges: 1/2 starch, 1 fruit

Acknowledgments

*The publisher would like to thank the companies and organizations
listed below for the use of their recipes and photographs
in this publication.*

Chilean Fresh Fruit Association

Colorado Potato Administrative Committee

Del Monte Corporation

Dole Food Company, Inc.

Equal® sweetener

Guiltless Gourmet®

The Hershey Company

Jennie-O Turkey Store®

National Honey Board

National Turkey Federation

North Dakota Wheat Commission

The Quaker® Oatmeal Kitchens

Reckitt Benckiser Inc.

SPLENDA® is a trademark of McNeil Nutritionals, LLC

The Sugar Association, Inc.

Unilever Foods North America

General Index

184 **Index**

Index **185**

Index **187**

Icon Index

LOW-CARB low carb

HIGH-FIBER high fiber

QUICK RECIPE *Quick Recipe*

meatless
MEATLESS

cooking for 1 or 2
COOKING FOR 1 OR 2

METRIC CONVERSION CHART

VOLUME MEASUREMENTS (dry)

1/8 teaspoon = 0.5 mL
1/4 teaspoon = 1 mL
1/2 teaspoon = 2 mL
3/4 teaspoon = 4 mL
1 teaspoon = 5 mL
1 tablespoon = 15 mL
2 tablespoons = 30 mL
1/4 cup = 60 mL
1/3 cup = 75 mL
1/2 cup = 125 mL
2/3 cup = 150 mL
3/4 cup = 175 mL
1 cup = 250 mL
2 cups = 1 pint = 500 mL
3 cups = 750 mL
4 cups = 1 quart = 1 L

VOLUME MEASUREMENTS (fluid)

1 fluid ounce (2 tablespoons) = 30 mL
4 fluid ounces (1/2 cup) = 125 mL
8 fluid ounces (1 cup) = 250 mL
12 fluid ounces (1 1/2 cups) = 375 mL
16 fluid ounces (2 cups) = 500 mL

WEIGHTS (mass)

1/2 ounce = 15 g
1 ounce = 30 g
3 ounces = 90 g
4 ounces = 120 g
8 ounces = 225 g
10 ounces = 285 g
12 ounces = 360 g
16 ounces = 1 pound = 450 g

DIMENSIONS

1/16 inch = 2 mm
1/8 inch = 3 mm
1/4 inch = 6 mm
1/2 inch = 1.5 cm
3/4 inch = 2 cm
1 inch = 2.5 cm

OVEN TEMPERATURES

250°F = 120°C
275°F = 140°C
300°F = 150°C
325°F = 160°C
350°F = 180°C
375°F = 190°C
400°F = 200°C
425°F = 220°C
450°F = 230°C

BAKING PAN SIZES

Utensil	Size in Inches/Quarts	Metric Volume	Size in Centimeters
Baking or Cake Pan (square or rectangular)	8×8×2	2 L	20×20×5
	9×9×2	2.5 L	23×23×5
	12×8×2	3 L	30×20×5
	13×9×2	3.5 L	33×23×5
Loaf Pan	8×4×3	1.5 L	20×10×7
	9×5×3	2 L	23×13×7
Round Layer Cake Pan	8×1½	1.2 L	20×4
	9×1½	1.5 L	23×4
Pie Plate	8×1¼	750 mL	20×3
	9×1¼	1 L	23×3
Baking Dish or Casserole	1 quart	1 L	—
	1½ quart	1.5 L	—
	2 quart	2 L	—

COUNTRY STORE

Our Newest Organizer for All Your Recipes

YOUR favorite "Clip & Keep" recipes will stay clean and organized in our new Taste of Home "Fruit & Flowers" binder. With its distinctive design, it's ideal for recipes from all of Reiman Publications' magazines. Plus, it comes with cooking charts and tips.

Hardcover, 2-ring binder has 50 clear sleeves for storing recipes, plus 25 blank recipe cards and nine divider pages. 6"W x 2"D x 7"H. Wipe-clean cover.

Save 10% When You Buy Two or More—Mix & Match

32835 Fruit & Flowers Recipe Binder…**$10.99 ea.**
$9.89 ea. (2 or more)
18968 Extra Binder Sleeves (25)…**$2.99 ea.**
$2.69 ea. (2 or more)
32870 Extra Recipe Cards (25)…**$3.99 ea.**
$3.59 ea. (2 or more)

Antique Look and Feel Outside, with the Latest Phone Features Inside!

GIVE your home the charming look of a 1920s farmhouse without sacrificing modern telephone conveniences. This authentic reproduction of a classic telephone has a hand-rubbed oak finish and brushed, bronze-plated hardware. The crank handle actually turns and the drawer opens for storage.

Modern conveniences include touch-tone buttons as well as hold, redial, speaker-phone and volume-control buttons. There are even key rings on the bottom! 17-1/2"H x 12-1/4"W x 7" deep.

33753 Country Kitchen Phone…**$99.99**

Wedgwood

Nonslip Latex Gripper

Hunter Green

Natural

Our Comfy Chair Pads Stay Seated

GIVE your kitchen chairs a face-lift with these soft chair pads. The 2" thick, foam-filled olefin pads provide comfort without those ties that always rip or come undone. Nonslip Gripper™ backing won't scratch furniture. They're easy to care for—just wipe clean. Choose from 16"W x 14"L or 18"W x 16"L. Available in colors shown.

31537 Slab Chair Pad (16"W x 14"L)…**$9.99**
BONUS: Four or more for only…**$7.99 each**
32343 Oversized Chair Pad (18"W x 16"L)…**$14.99**
BONUS: Four or more for only…**$11.99 each**

Tines are grooved!

Grooved Forks Grab Spaghetti

EATING delicious pasta dishes is now a lot easier! The tines on these unique, stainless-steel forks are specially grooved to grab and hold spaghetti strands and other types of pasta. Food stays on the fork so it doesn't slip and spatter your clothes. Measures 7-1/8"L x 7/8"W each.

32759 Spaghetti Forks (set of eight)…**$12.99**

Come Home to a Tasty Meal, Ready for You!

GREAT for stews and other one-pot meals, Taste of Home's 1-1/2-quart slow cooker gives you home-cooked results without having to be home. The removable stoneware crock is dishwasher-safe, too! Features low, high and keep-warm settings plus stay-cool handles for easy moving. You can check on your recipe without lifting the see-through tempered glass lid.

32839 Taste of Home's 1-1/2-Quart Slow Cooker…**$16.99**

Spring

Easter

Thanksgiving

Fourth of July

Halloween

Christmas

Our Brand-New Dress-a-Pig Helps You "Ham It Up" for the Holidays

SHOW your friends that everyone at your place is in the spirit of the season—including "Priscilla" Pig. Place her by your door as a friendly greeter, or on a table as a whimsical decoration.

She comes with six hat and cape outfits for all your favorite holidays and seasonal themes: Halloween, Thanksgiving, Christmas, Easter, Spring and Fourth of July. She's hand-painted on detailed poly resin. 11" x 5" x 7".

33769 Dress-a-Pig with Six Outfits…**$16.99**

33" fully extended

Folds for storage to a convenient 17"

High or Low, This Tool Can Reach It!

BENDING, climbing and straining are distant memories with this amazing Gopher. It extends your reach almost 3 feet and picks up everything from cracker boxes to paper clips. Easy-squeeze handle and suction cups provide a steady grip. Sturdy, lightweight aluminum pole folds for storage in a drawer.

32231 Gopher™ Pick Up & Reaching Tool…**$12.99**
BONUS: Two or more…**$9.99 each**

Pumps Dishwashing Soap Directly into Your Sink

NO MORE touching sticky bottles of dishwashing liquid. This 8"H pump bottle has an extra-long, 3" spout that squirts just the right amount into dishwater or a pan to soak! Wide neck for easy filling. Nonskid base. Acrylic bottle holds 12-1/2 ounces.

33484 Kitchen Soap Dispenser…**$9.99**

Dry a "Sink Full" with Our Giant Flour Sack Towels

ABSOLUTELY the best dish towels we've ever used! These large, absorbent towels dry a lot of dishes and dry out fast. Set of six 29" x 28" 100% cotton towels. Imported.

30628 Flour Sack Towels (set of six)…**$12.99**

Its Voice Tells You How Far You Walked

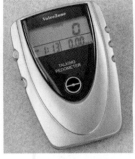

TALKING pedometer counts up to 99,999 steps, and based on your stride length, it "tells" the total distance you have walked. Press a button and clock announces time. Four-sound alarm, plus seven tunes that keep time with your pace. On/off switch for alarm and music! 2-1/4"L x 1-5/8"W.

32959 Talking Pedometer…**$12.99**

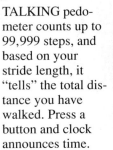

Your Armchair Becomes an "Instant Desk"

OUR lightweight, portable Lap Board becomes a "desk" in seconds. Just place it across the arms of your favorite chair! Easily write letters, play card games or eat a snack—with no pressure on your legs. Elastic straps keep papers in place. Strong plywood provides a secure, balanced surface. Wipe-clean laminated finish. 31"L x 12-1/2"W x 3/16"H.

32039 Lap Board…**$9.99**

They Make Cleaning So Easy

VERSATILE microfiber cloths clean without chemicals or soap. Each 12-1/2" square cloth absorbs *seven times* its weight as it scrubs grime, polishes glass and more. When dry, it picks up dust like a magnet. Machine wash.

33840 Miracle Cloths (multi-colored set of four, as shown)…**$9.99**

2

- Stick-resistant
- Ready to use right away
- Superior heat distribution
- Superior quality, U.S.-craftsmanship

Whip Up Skillets Full of Old-Time Southern Flavor

OVER 230 recipes like "Tender Cube Steak with Mushroom Gravy" and "Fried Corn" are so down-home delicious and easy to make! You get main dishes, sides, stews, breads and more. Softcover, 195 pages with nostalgic illustrations. 6" x 8-1/2".

34080 *A Skillet Full* Cookbook…**$19.99**

Grater Spoon Does Double Duty

NO need to bring out the cheese grater… use the grater built into this spoon! Quickly add grated cheese to any dish without dirtying another gadget. Stainless-steel serving spoon is slotted for draining, too. Choose from two sizes.

34074 12-1/2"L Grater Spoon…**$8.99**
34075 10"L Grater Spoon…**$6.99**

Pot-Notch Works Like a Built-in Spoon Rest

DRIPS just fall back into the pan thanks to the newest design in wooden spoons! Special notches in the handles let you hang these spoons on the edge of your pan. No more messy stovetops!

Set of three 12"L birch spoons includes basting spoon, spatula and slotted spoon. Hand wash.

33565 Wooden Spoons (set of three)…**$9.99**

Slicing Your Veggies Is A Cinch

STEEL slicer makes uniform veggie slices with no struggle. Sharp blade adjusts to nine thicknesses for slicing coleslaw, cucumbers and more. 7-1/2"L x 4"W x 2-1/2"H.

32379 Platform Slicer…**$8.99**

Revolutionary Cast-Iron Cookware Comes "Pre-Seasoned"…and Stays That Way!

EVEN though this skillet, Dutch oven and grill pan are U.S.-made of cast iron, you won't have to spend hours seasoning them to create stick-resistant surfaces.

That's because each one has been treated with a unique vegetable oil solution that's already baked in…and stays on for years of use. Skillet is 12"D x 2" deep. Five-quart Dutch oven with lid measures 10-3/4"D x 4" deep. Grill pan is 10-1/2"D x 1-3/4" deep and features a special "raised" cooking surface that allows fat to drip off food. Enjoy cast-iron cooking without extra work!

34284 Cast-Iron 12" Skillet…**$21.99**
34283 Cast-Iron 5-Qt. Dutch Oven…**$39.99**
34285 Cast-Iron 10-1/2" Grill Pan…**$21.99**

Cooks Love These New Broiler Pans

SURE, your old oven came with its standard-issue broiler pan, but these nonstick ones are better! Their unique "handled" racks are much easier to wash because they have holes instead of angled slots. Heavy-gauge steel construction. Choose two handy sizes: 11" x 14" and 7" x 11".

33260 Large Broiler Pan…**$19.99**
33259 Small Broiler Pan…**$12.99**

Select and Measure Your Spices with Ease

HANDY spice carousel rotates on a base you can mount under a cabinet or set on a counter.

Each of the 12 containers dispenses the exact amount needed. Turn the dial one click for every 1/4 teaspoon, and the spice sprinkles out (see photo). Shaker tops and spoon-wide ports, too!

Each plastic carousel includes 55 pre-printed and four blank labels. Buy two and stack 'em (as shown). 8-1/2"W x 4"H each. Spices not included.

33717 Select-a-Spice…**$29.99**
BONUS: Two or more for…**$24.99 each**

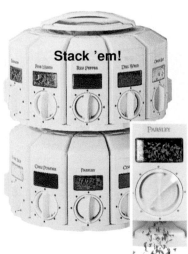

Stack 'em!

Dispenses the exact amount

"Chirp Chirp"

Your Bird-Watching Friends Will Flock Around This Clock!

EACH HOUR, one of 12 North American birds sings its song on our Audubon™ Bird Clock. Light sensor deactivates sounds at night. Mounts easily on a wall. 13-1/2"D. ABS plastic. Three AA batteries, not included.

33859 Audubon Bird Clock…**$29.99**

Wearable Timer Lets You Leave the Kitchen

ENJOY more freedom with the "Timer on a Rope". A 16" cord lets you hang it around your neck. Made of 2-1/2"D lightweight plastic. Times up to one hour. Magnetic back lets you stick it on the fridge!

32981 Timer on a Rope…**$5.99**

Taste of Home's Handy Skillet Performs Personal-Sized Cooking Feats

SCRAMBLE EGGS, saute onions or grill a sandwich fast with our favorite mini fry pan. The 6-3/4"D, nonstick cooking surface is sized right for smaller servings. Includes an adjustable heat control (to 425°F) and see-through glass lid. 600 watts.

32750 Taste of Home's Quick Fry Electric Skillet…**$24.99**

Taste of Home *Exclusive*

Cutting Board Gives Your Countertop a Fresh Look

BRIGHT red and juicy-looking apples printed on this cutting board liven up *and protect* your countertop. Tempered glass stands up to cutting, chopping and dicing and is more hygienic than plastic or wood. Great for resting hot dishes just out of the oven, too! Features rubber nonslip "feet". 15-5/8"L x 11-3/4"W.

33725 Apple Cutting Board…**$12.99**

$7.99 Value

FREE GIFT With your order!

WE APPRECIATE your business so much, we'll gladly send you this 3-in-1 Flashlight—a $7.99 value—with your order. It's a reading light, flashlight and emergency flasher all in one. Best of all, this 3-in-1 Flashlight is YOURS FREE with your Country Store order.

(Supplies are limited. We reserve the right to substitute gifts of equal or greater value.)

CHARGE ORDERS CALL TOLL-FREE
1-800/558-1013
Fax: 1-414/423-3901

PHONE HOURS:
Monday-Friday 7 a.m. to 10 p.m. and Saturday 8 a.m. to 3:30 p.m., Central Time. Mention Suite 7245.

Place Your Order On-Line at CountryStoreCatalog.com

ORDER BY MAIL OR PHONE US TOLL-FREE. To order by mail use this handy form and send to the address below. You can charge by mail or phone if you're a Visa, Master Card, Discover/NOVUS or American Express cardholder.

COUNTRY HANDSHAKE GUARANTEE. Every Country Store item is fully guaranteed. If you're not completely satisfied, simply return it and we'll refund your purchase price, no questions asked.

METHOD OF PAYMENT:
❑ Check (made out to Country Store; sorry, no C.O.D.s)
OR CHARGE:
❑ Visa ❑ Master Card
❑ Discover/NOVUS ❑ American Express

Carefully write in your **ACCOUNT NUMBER** (all digits)

Exp. Date_____

Signature_____
(required if using credit card)

Mail order to:
COUNTRY STORE
Suite 7245, 5925 Country Lane
PO Box 990, Greendale WI 53129-0990

COUNTRY STORE ORDER FORM

ORDERED BY:
Your Name _____
(please print)

Address_____

City _____ State _____

Zip _____ Phone ( )
(We will telephone ONLY if we have a question about your order.)

ITEM CODE	DESCRIPTION OF ITEM *(please print)*	SIZE	PRICE EACH	HOW MANY	TOTAL
40170	FREE Gift – 3-in-1 Flashlight		$7.99	1	FREE!

Need more space? Please use separate sheet.

ONLY $1.99 SHIPPING ON ALL ORDERS!

SHIPPING AND HANDLING CHART:

$1.99 ON ALL ORDERS

1. Total Order	
2. *All orders add Shipping/Handling from chart at left	$1.99
3. Add lines 1 and 2	
4. If shipped to Wis., add 5% of line 3 for state sales tax	
5. TOTAL AMOUNT DUE	

PLEASE NOTE: Prices guaranteed through March 2005. Orders from outside the U.S. are accepted by credit card or Postal Money Order in U.S. funds ONLY and must double shipping and handling charges. Offer not valid on previous orders or in combination with other promotions.

Suite 7245

4